Visual Guide
Campbell Media Manager for

Essential Biology

Third Edition

and

Essential Biology
with Physiology

Second Edition

Campbell • Reece • Simon

PEARSON

Benjamin
Cummings

San Francisco Boston New York
Cape Town Hong Kong London Madrid Mexico City
Montreal Munich Paris Singapore Sydney Tokyo Toronto

Executive Editor: Beth Wilbur
Senior Acquisitions Editor: Chalon Bridges
Director of Development: Deborah Gale
Developmental Editor: Evelyn Dahlgren
Project Editor: Ginnie Simione-Jutson
Director, Media Development: Lauren Fogel
Media Producer: Jonathan Ballard
Managing Editor, Production: Mike Early
Media Technology Supervisor: Jennifer Mattson
Manufacturing Buyer: Stacy Wong
Executive Marketing Manager: Lauren Harp
PowerPoint Lectures Author: Chris Romero, Front Range Community College, Larimer Campus
PowerPoint Lectures Editor: John Hammett
Art Proofer: Pete Shanks
Production Services: Progressive Information Technologies
Printer: Courier Company

ISBN 0-8053-0435-5
ISBN-13 978-0-80530-435-0

2 3 4 5 6 7 8 9-CRS-09 08 07

www.aw-bc.com

Preface

The new Visual Guide to the Media manager is a chapter-by-chapter visual archive of more than 2,500 images for the exclusive use of adopters of *Essential Biology,* Third Edition and *Essential Biology with Physiology,* Second Edition, by Campbell, Reece, and Simon. All of the diverse visual resources—art, tables, photos, videos, and animations—are organized by chapter. All file formats have been thoroughly tested in large lecture halls.

The following instructor and student media is organized by chapter:

Instructor Resources

Image Library

- All art from the text, with and without labels
- Over 1000 photos from the text and other sources
- All tables from the text

PowerPoint® Library & Lecture Outlines

- PowerPoint® Label Edit Art Slides with editable labels and leaders; also includes photos and tables from the text
- PowerPoint® Step Edit Art for step-by-step presentation, with editable labels and leaders *(see grid)*
- PowerPoint® Prepared Lectures; includes concise lecture outlines with all figures and tables; also includes links to animations and videos
- PowerPoint® Active Lecture ("Clicker") Questions for use with Classroom Response System
- PowerPoint® Lectures for Scientific American Current Issues in Biology *(see grid)*
- PowerPoint® Quiz Show Lecture Questions with chapter content in an interactive classroom game show format

Media Library

- 90 videos in Flash and MPEG formats on web *(see grid)*
- Over 148 animations in Flash format *(see grid)*

Additional Resources

- Test Bank in Word Format
- Instructor's Guide to Text and Media in Word format
- Media Manager Quick Reference Guide
- Graph It! (Instructor Version)
- Case Studies in the Process of Science Answers
- Video Scripts
- Extra photo captions

Student Resources

7 eTutors *(see grid)*

22 MP3 Tutors *(see grid)*

51 Discovery Channel Video Clips

7 You Decide *(see grid)*

11 Graph It! *(see grid)*

138 Activities *(see grid)*

52 Case Studies in the Process of Science investigations

E-book

Cumulative Test for self-assessment on multiple chapters

12 LabBench activities with animations and interactive questions

eTutor Acknowledgments

eTutor Storyboards
Russell Chun
Pat Burner
Brad Williamson, Olathe East High School

eTutor Animations
Animated Biomedical Productions, Westmead, Australia

eTutor reviewers
Jane Reece, University of California, Berkeley
Lisa Urry, Mills College
Mitch Albers, Minneapolis College
Gretchen Bernard, Moraine Valley Community College
Uriel Buitrago-Suarez, Harper College
Nancy Butler, Kutztown University
Guy A. Caldwell, The University of Alabama
Kim Caldwell, The University of Alabama
Gerald G. Farr, Texas State University
Sandra Gibbons, Moraine Valley Community College
Kelly Hogan, The University of North Carolina at Chapel Hill
Cody Locke, The University of Alabama
Marvin Brandon Lowery, Sam Houston State University
David Mirman, Mt. San Antonio College
James Newcomb, New England College
Tom Owens, Cornell University
Mitch Price, The Pennsylvania State University
David A. Rintoul, Kansas State University
Renee Rivas, The University of Alabama
Juliet Spencer, University of San Francisco
Beth Stall, El Centro College
Diane Sweeney, Crystal Springs Uplands School
Jamey Thompson, Hudson Valley Community College
Miriam Zolan, Indiana University
Michelle Zurawski, Moraine Valley Community College

Contents

UNIT SIX: Plant Structure and Function

Chapter 1 Introduction: Biology Today

01_00aPufferFish_LP.jpg

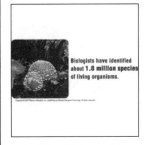

01_00bCell_LP.jpg

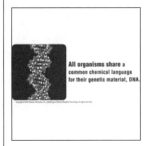

01_00cForestMushrooms_LP.jpg

01_00dDNA_L.jpg

01_01-BioInTheNews_L.jpg

01_01-BioInTheNews_U.jpg

01_01aBioInTheNews_UP.jpg

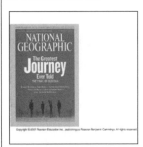

01_01bBioInTheNews_UP.jpg

01_01cBioInTheNews_UP.jpg

01_01dBioInTheNews_UP.jpg

01_01eBioInTheNews_UP.jpg

01_01fBioInTheNews_UP.jpg

01_01gBioInTheNews_UP.jpg

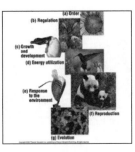

01_02-LifeCharacteristic_LP.jpg

01_02-LifeCharacteristic_UP.jpg

01_02aLifeCharacteristic_LP.jpg

01_02aLifeCharacteristic_UP.jpg

01_02ax1OrderCollage_XUP.jpg

01_02ax2OrderButterfly_XUP.jpg

01_02ax3OrderNautilus_XUP.jpg

01_02ax4OrderGaillardi_XUP.jpg

01_02ax5OrderXylem_XUP.jpg

01_02bLifeCharacteristic_LP.jpg

01_02bLifeCharacteristic_UP.jpg

01_02cLifeCharacteristic_LP.jpg

01_02cLifeCharacteristic_UP.jpg

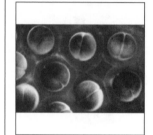

01_02cx1DevelopFrogEgg_XUP.jpg

01_02cx2DevelopSeedlin_XUP.jpg

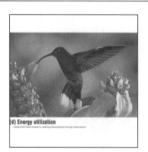

01_02dLifeCharacteristic_LP.jpg

01_02dLifeCharacteristic_UP.jpg

01_02dx1EnergySunlight_XUP.jpg

01_02dx2EnergyMosquito_XUP.jpg

01_02eLifeCharacteristic_LP.jpg

01_02eLifeCharacteristic_UP.jpg

01_02fLifeCharacteristic_LP.jpg

01_02fLifeCharacteristic_UP.jpg

01_02fx1ReproBeetles_XUP.jpg

01_02fx2ReproBacteria_XUP.jpg

01_02fx3ReproLily_XUP.jpg

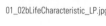
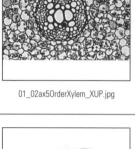

01_02gLifeCharacteristic_LP.jpg

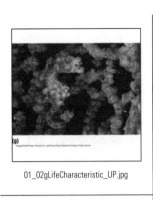

01_02gLifeCharacteristic_UP.jpg

01_02gSeaHorses_SV.mpg

01_02gSeaHorses_VT.swf

01_02gx1EvolCollage_XUP.jpg

01_02gx2Poorwill_XUP.jpg

01_03Biosphere_1_CL.jpg

01_03Biosphere_1_CNL.jpg

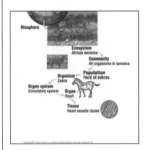

01_03Biosphere_2_CL.jpg

01_03Biosphere_2_CNL.jpg

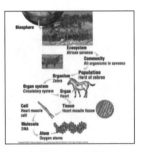

01_03Biosphere_3_CL.jpg

01_03Biosphere_3_CNL.jpg

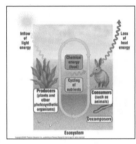

01_04EcosysEnergyFlow_L.jpg

01_04EcosysEnergyFlow_U.jpg

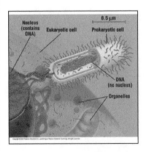

01_05_ProVsEukaryoticCell_L.jpg

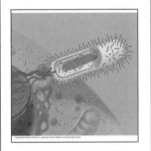

01_05_ProVsEukaryoticCell_U.jpg

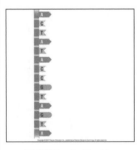

01_06DNAnucleotides_L.jpg

01_07DNAbiotechnology_UP.jpg

01_08BioDiversity_UP.jpg

01_09-ThreeDomains_LP.jpg

01_09-ThreeDomains_UP.jpg

01_09aThreeDomains_LP.jpg

01_09aThreeDomains_UP.jpg

01_09bThreeDomains_LP.jpg

01_09bThreeDomains_UP.jpg

01_09cThreeDomains_LP.jpg

01_09cThreeDomains_UP.jpg

01_09dThreeDomains_LP.jpg

01_09dThreeDomains_UP.jpg

01_09eThreeDomains_LP.jpg

01_09eThreeDomains_UP.jpg

01_09fThreeDomains_LP.jpg

01_09fThreeDomains_UP.jpg

01_10DinosaurFossil_UP.jpg

01_11BearPhylogeny_L.jpg

01_11BearPhylogeny_U.jpg

01_12Darwin_L.jpg

01_12xOriginOfSpecies_XUP.jpg

01_13GalapagosFinches_L.jpg

01_13GalapagosFinches_U.jpg

01_14-NaturalSelection_L.jpg

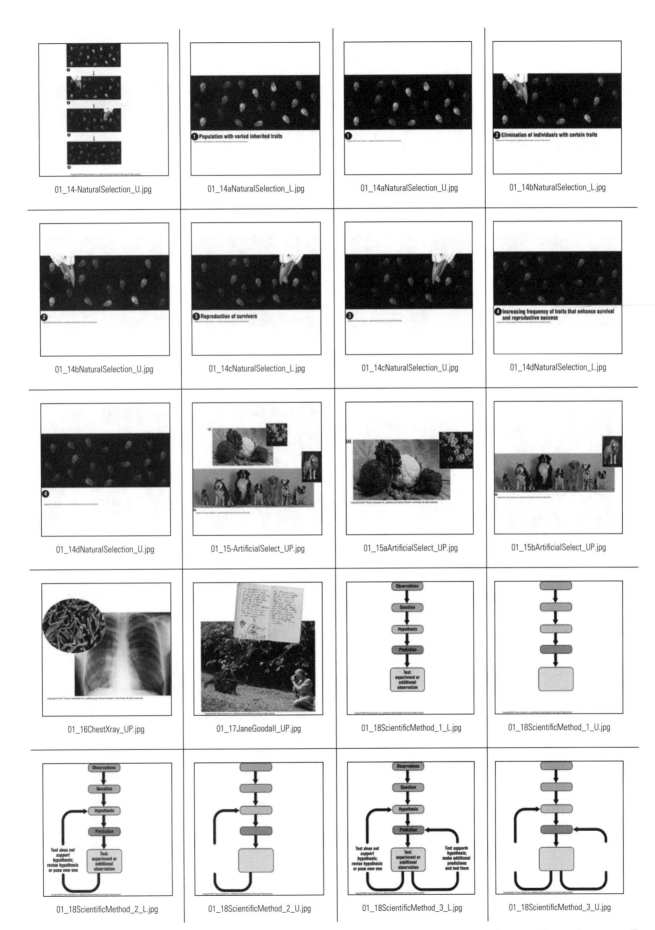

01_14-NaturalSelection_U.jpg

01_14aNaturalSelection_L.jpg

01_14aNaturalSelection_U.jpg

01_14bNaturalSelection_L.jpg

01_14bNaturalSelection_U.jpg

01_14cNaturalSelection_L.jpg

01_14cNaturalSelection_U.jpg

01_14dNaturalSelection_L.jpg

01_14dNaturalSelection_U.jpg

01_15-ArtificialSelect_UP.jpg

01_15aArtificialSelect_UP.jpg

01_15bArtificialSelect_UP.jpg

01_16ChestXray_UP.jpg

01_17JaneGoodall_UP.jpg

01_18ScientificMethod_1_L.jpg

01_18ScientificMethod_1_U.jpg

01_18ScientificMethod_2_L.jpg

01_18ScientificMethod_2_U.jpg

01_18ScientificMethod_3_L.jpg

01_18ScientificMethod_3_U.jpg

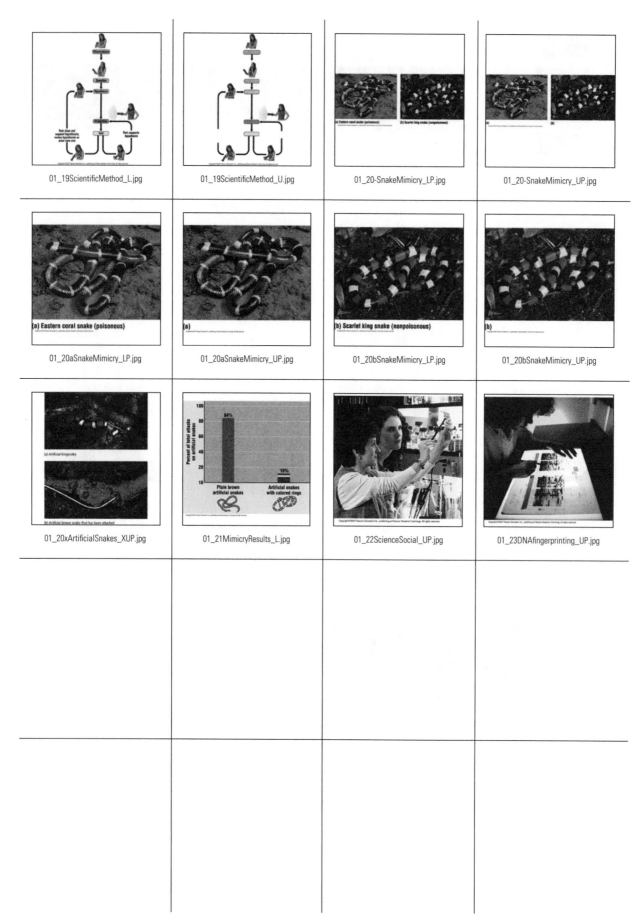

01_19ScientificMethod_L.jpg

01_19ScientificMethod_U.jpg

01_20-SnakeMimicry_LP.jpg

01_20-SnakeMimicry_UP.jpg

01_20aSnakeMimicry_LP.jpg

01_20aSnakeMimicry_UP.jpg

01_20bSnakeMimicry_LP.jpg

01_20bSnakeMimicry_UP.jpg

01_20xArtificialSnakes_XUP.jpg

01_21MimicryResults_L.jpg

01_22ScienceSocial_UP.jpg

01_23DNAfingerprinting_UP.jpg

Chapter 2 Essential Chemistry for Biology

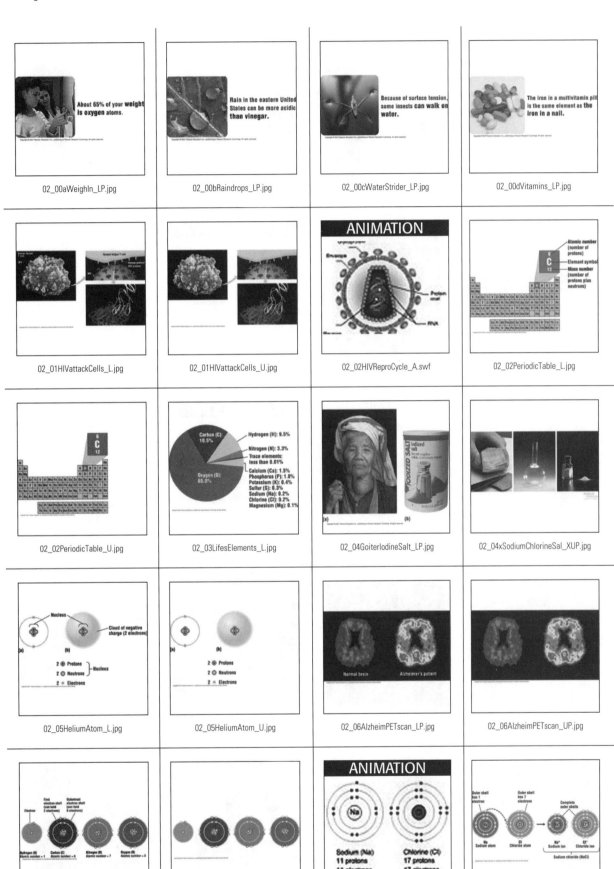

02_00aWeighIn_LP.jpg

02_00bRaindrops_LP.jpg

02_00cWaterStrider_LP.jpg

02_00dVitamins_LP.jpg

02_01HIVattackCells_L.jpg

02_01HIVattackCells_U.jpg

02_02HIVReproCycle_A.swf

02_02PeriodicTable_L.jpg

02_02PeriodicTable_U.jpg

02_03LifesElements_L.jpg

02_04GoiterIodineSalt_LP.jpg

02_04xSodiumChlorineSal_XUP.jpg

02_05HeliumAtom_L.jpg

02_05HeliumAtom_U.jpg

02_06AlzheimPETscan_LP.jpg

02_06AlzheimPETscan_UP.jpg

02_07LifesElements_L.jpg

02_07LifesElements_U.jpg

02_08IonicBonds_A.swf

02_08-IonicBondFormation_L.jpg

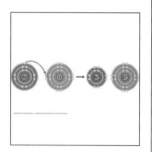
02_08-IonicBondFormation_U.jpg

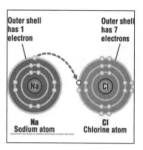
02_08aIonicBondFormation_L.jpg

02_08aIonicBondFormation_U.jpg

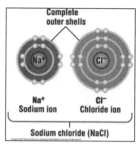
02_08bIonicBondFormation_L.jpg

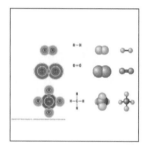
02_08bIonicBondFormation_U.jpg

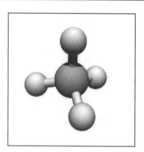
02_08xSaltCrystal_XUP.jpg

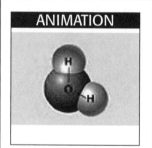
02_09CovalentBonds_A.swf

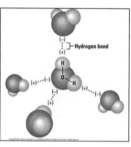
02_09MoleculeRepresent_L.jpg

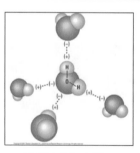
02_09MoleculeRepresent_U.jpg

02_09xMethaneBallStick_XUP.jpg

02_10WaterStructure_A.swf

02_10PolarMolecule_L.jpg

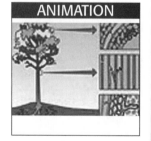
02_10PolarMolecule_U.jpg

02_11EarthWaterWorld_UP.jpg

02_11x1WaterCollage_XUP.jpg

02_11x2IceFishing_XUP.jpg

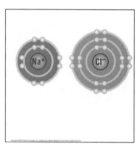
02_12WaterTransport_A.swf

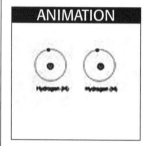
02_12Cohesion_CL.jpg

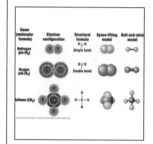
02_12Cohesion_CNL.jpg

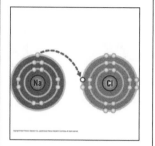
02_12xTreeCohesionWater_XUP.jpg

02_13SurfaceTension_UP.jpg

02_14EvaporativeCooling_UP.jpg

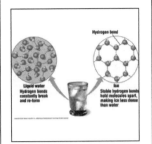

02_15HbondsIceFloats_L.jpg

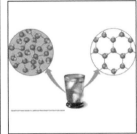

02_15HbondsIceFloats_U.jpg

02_15x1WaterMolecularMo_XUP.jpg

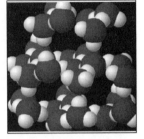

02_15x2IceMolecularMode_XUP.jpg

02_15x3FrozenWaterBenze_XUP.jpg

02_16SaltInWater_L.jpg

02_16SaltInWater_U.jpg

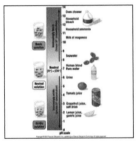

02_17pHscale_L.jpg

02_17pHscale_U.jpg

02_18AcidPrecipitation_UP.jpg

02_18x1AcidRainTreeDama_XUP.jpg

02_18x2Smokestacks_XUP.jpg

02_19Volcanism_L.jpg

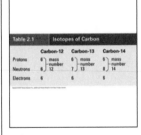

02_T01IsotopesTable_T.jpg

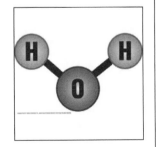

02_UN26Water_U.jpg

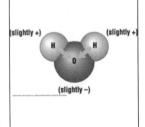

02_UN27aHydrogenBond_L.jpg

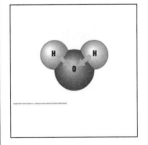

02_UN27aHydrogenBond_U.jpg

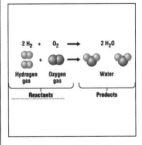

02_UN27bChemicalReact_L.jpg

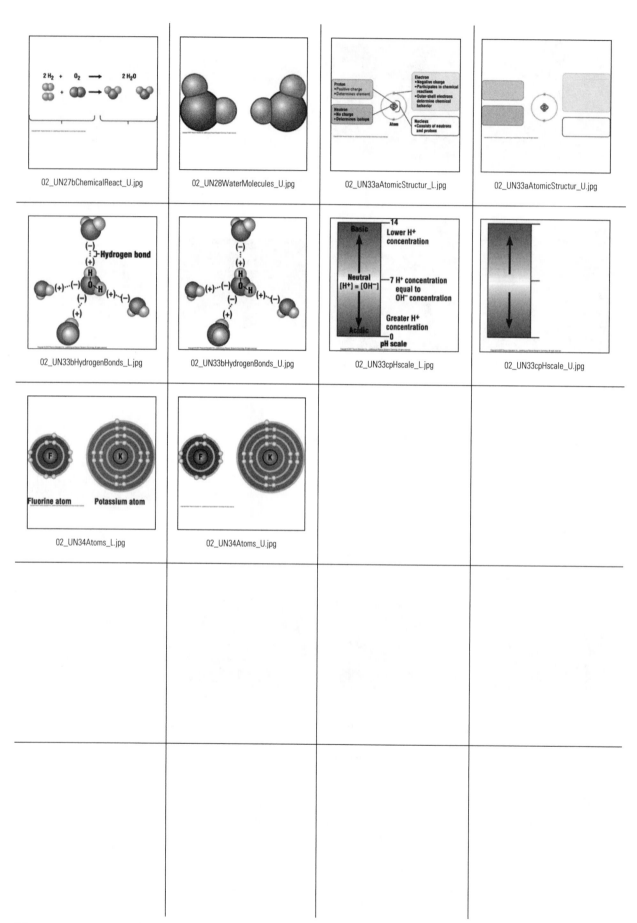

02_UN27bChemicalReact_U.jpg

02_UN28WaterMolecules_U.jpg

02_UN33aAtomicStructur_L.jpg

02_UN33aAtomicStructur_U.jpg

02_UN33bHydrogenBonds_L.jpg

02_UN33bHydrogenBonds_U.jpg

02_UN33cpHscale_L.jpg

02_UN33cpHscale_U.jpg

02_UN34Atoms_L.jpg

02_UN34Atoms_U.jpg

Chapter 3 The Molecules of Life

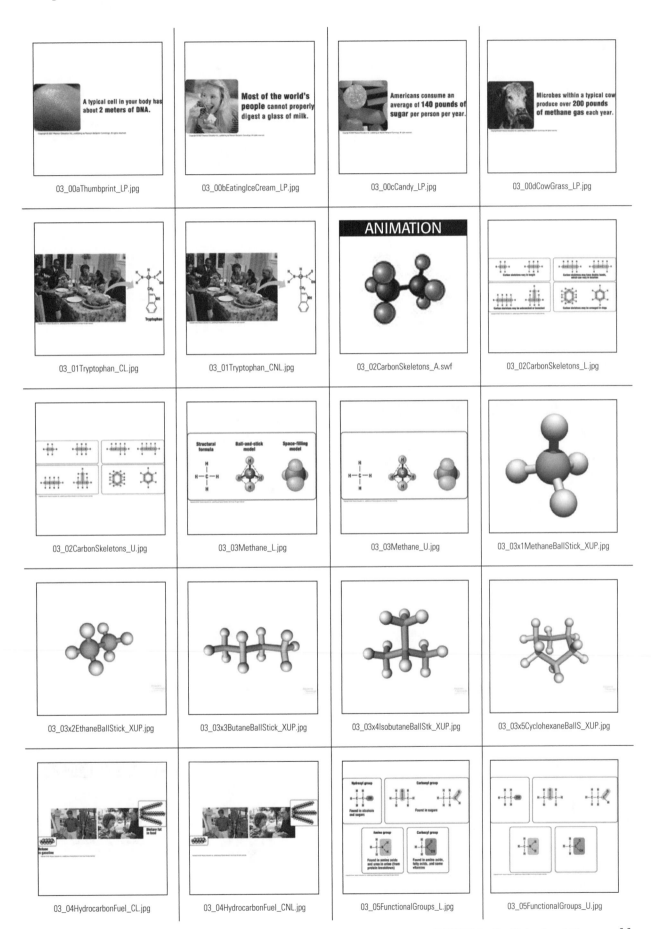

03_00aThumbprint_LP.jpg

03_00bEatingIceCream_LP.jpg

03_00cCandy_LP.jpg

03_00dCowGrass_LP.jpg

03_01Tryptophan_CL.jpg

03_01Tryptophan_CNL.jpg

03_02CarbonSkeletons_A.swf

03_02CarbonSkeletons_L.jpg

03_02CarbonSkeletons_U.jpg

03_03Methane_L.jpg

03_03Methane_U.jpg

03_03x1MethaneBallStick_XUP.jpg

03_03x2EthaneBallStick_XUP.jpg

03_03x3ButaneBallStick_XUP.jpg

03_03x4IsobutaneBallStk_XUP.jpg

03_03x5CyclohexaneBallS_XUP.jpg

03_04HydrocarbonFuel_CL.jpg

03_04HydrocarbonFuel_CNL.jpg

03_05FunctionalGroups_L.jpg

03_05FunctionalGroups_U.jpg

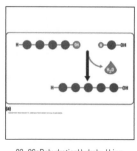

ANIMATION

03_06Polymers_A.swf

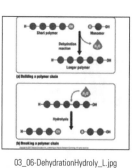

03_06-DehydrationHydroly_L.jpg

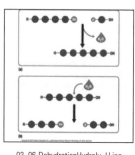

03_06-DehydrationHydroly_U.jpg

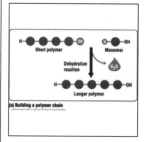

03_06aDehydrationHydroly_L.jpg

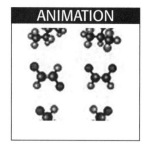

03_06aDehydrationHydroly_U.jpg

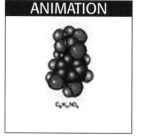

03_06bDehydrationHydroly_L.jpg

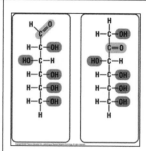

03_06bDehydrationHydroly_U.jpg

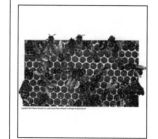

03_07BeeHoney_UP.jpg

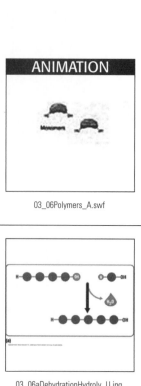

ANIMATION

03_08Isomers_A.swf

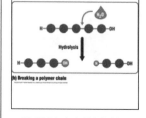

ANIMATION

03_08L_Dopa_A.swf

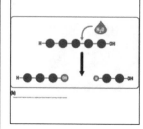

03_08MonosacchIsomers_L.jpg

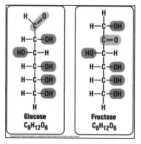

03_08MonosacchIsomers_U.jpg

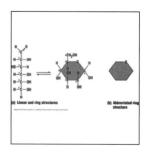

03_09-GlucoseStructure_L.jpg

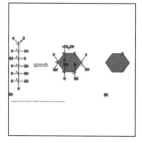

03_09-GlucoseStructure_U.jpg

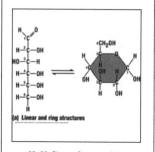

03_09aGlucoseStructure_L.jpg

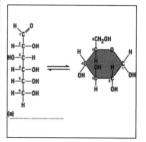

03_09aGlucoseStructure_U.jpg

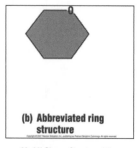

(b) Abbreviated ring structure

03_09bGlucoseStructure_L.jpg

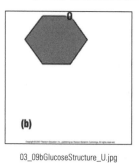

(b)

03_09bGlucoseStructure_U.jpg

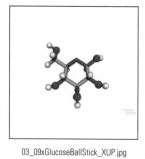

03_09xGlucoseBallStick_XUP.jpg

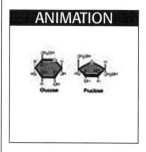

ANIMATION

03_10Disaccharides_A.swf

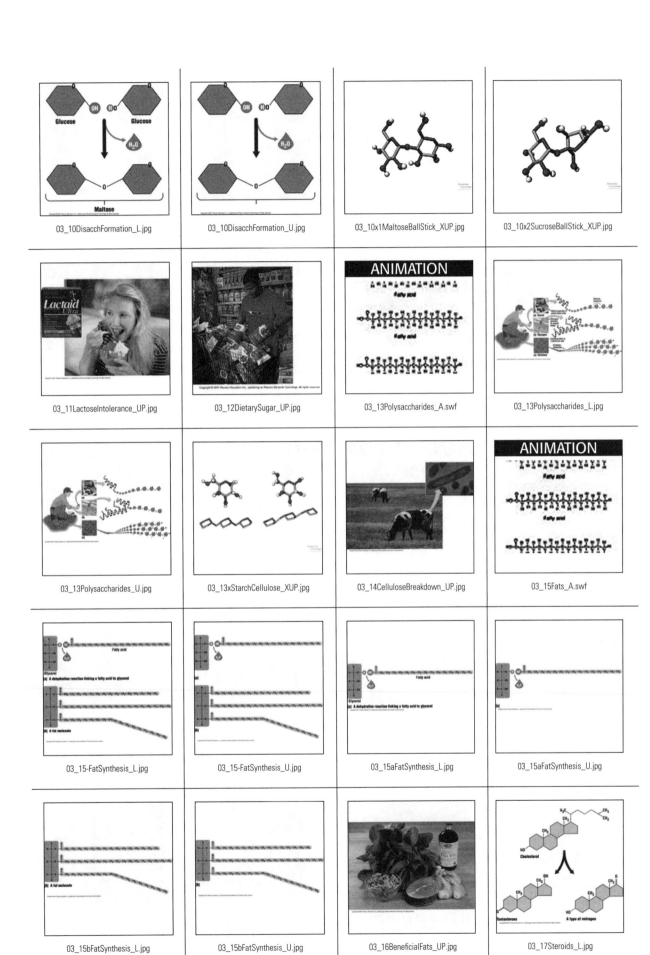

03_10DisacchFormation_L.jpg

03_10DisacchFormation_U.jpg

03_10x1MaltoseBallStick_XUP.jpg

03_10x2SucroseBallStick_XUP.jpg

03_11LactoseIntolerance_UP.jpg

03_12DietarySugar_UP.jpg

03_13Polysaccharides_A.swf

03_13Polysaccharides_L.jpg

03_13Polysaccharides_U.jpg

03_13xStarchCellulose_XUP.jpg

03_14CelluloseBreakdown_UP.jpg

03_15Fats_A.swf

03_15-FatSynthesis_L.jpg

03_15-FatSynthesis_U.jpg

03_15aFatSynthesis_L.jpg

03_15aFatSynthesis_U.jpg

03_15bFatSynthesis_L.jpg

03_15bFatSynthesis_U.jpg

03_16BeneficialFats_UP.jpg

03_17Steroids_L.jpg

03_17Steroids_U.jpg

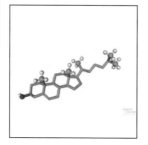

03_17xCholesterolBallSt_XUP.jpg

03_18JoseCanseco_UP.jpg

03_19aStructuralProteins_A.swf

03_19bStorageProteins_A.swf

03_19cContractileProtein_A.swf

03_19dTransportProteins_A.swf

03_19eDefensiveProteins_A.swf

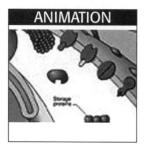

03_19fReceptorProteins_A.swf

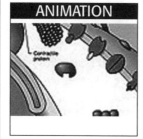

03_19gEnzymes_A.swf

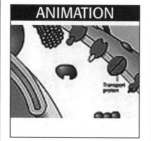

03_19hHormonalProteins_A.swf

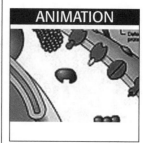

03_19iSensoryProteins_A.swf

03_19jGeneRegulatoryProt_A.swf

03_19-Proteins_LP.jpg

03_19-Proteins_UP.jpg

03_19aProteins_LP.jpg

03_19aProteins_UP.jpg

03_19bProteins_LP.jpg

03_19bProteins_UP.jpg

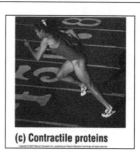

03_19cProteins_LP.jpg

03_19cProteins_UP.jpg

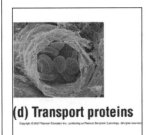

(d) Transport proteins

03_19dProteins_LP.jpg

(d)

03_19dProteins_UP.jpg

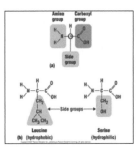

03_20-AminoAcidStructr_L.jpg

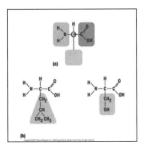

03_20-AminoAcidStructr_U.jpg

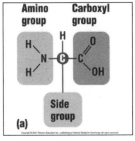

03_20aAminoAcidStructr_L.jpg

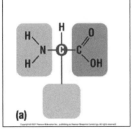

03_20aAminoAcidStructr_U.jpg

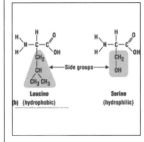

03_20bAminoAcidStructr_L.jpg

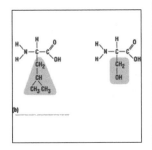

03_20bAminoAcidStructr_U.jpg

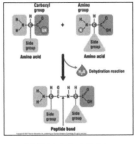

03_21JoinAminoAcid_L.jpg

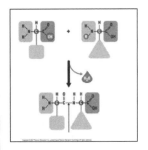

03_21JoinAminoAcid_U.jpg

03_22ProtPrimStructur_L.jpg

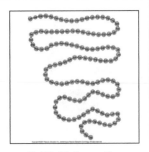

03_22ProtPrimStructur_U.jpg

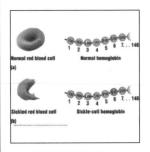

03_23SickleCellHb_CL.jpg

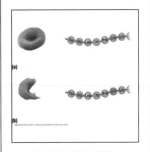

03_23SickleCellHb_CNL.jpg

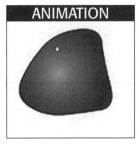

03_24aIntroProteinStruct_A.swf

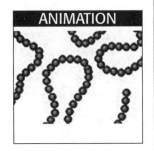

03_24aPrimaryStructure_A.swf

03_24bSecondaryStructure_A.swf

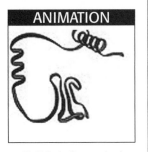

03_24cTertiaryStructure_A.swf

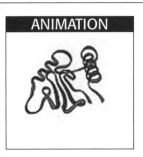

03_24dQuaternaryStructur_A.swf

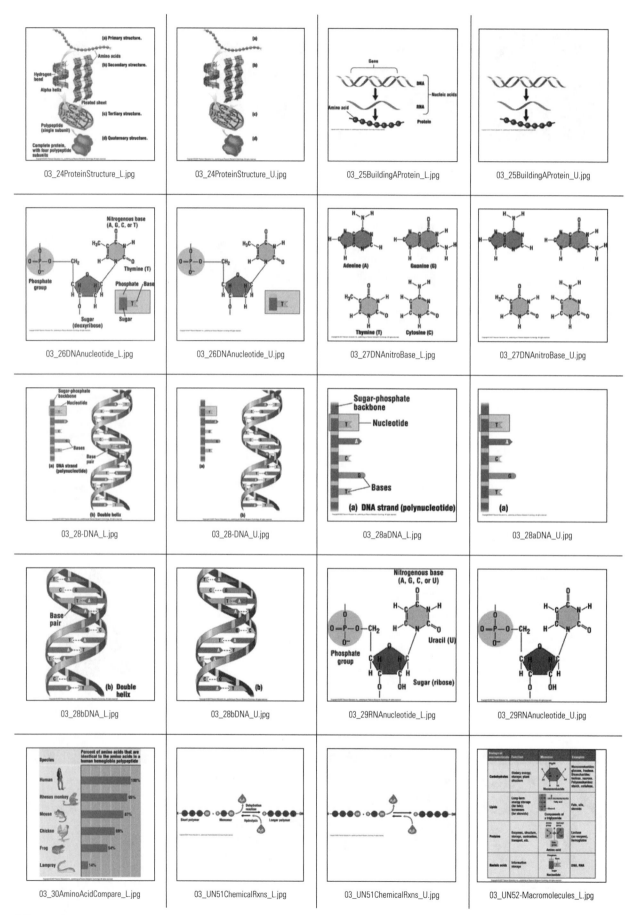

03_24ProteinStructure_L.jpg

03_24ProteinStructure_U.jpg

03_25BuildingAProtein_L.jpg

03_25BuildingAProtein_U.jpg

03_26DNAnucleotide_L.jpg

03_26DNAnucleotide_U.jpg

03_27DNAnitroBase_L.jpg

03_27DNAnitroBase_U.jpg

03_28-DNA_L.jpg

03_28-DNA_U.jpg

03_28aDNA_L.jpg

03_28aDNA_U.jpg

03_28bDNA_L.jpg

03_28bDNA_U.jpg

03_29RNAnucleotide_L.jpg

03_29RNAnucleotide_U.jpg

03_30AminoAcidCompare_L.jpg

03_UN51ChemicalRxns_L.jpg

03_UN51ChemicalRxns_U.jpg

03_UN52-Macromolecules_L.jpg

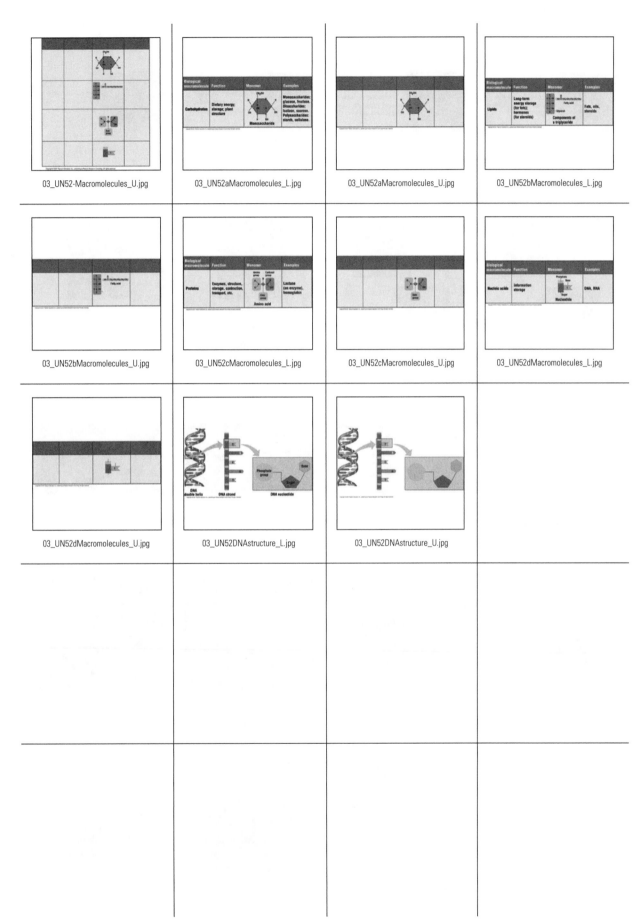

03_UN52-Macromolecules_U.jpg   03_UN52aMacromolecules_L.jpg   03_UN52aMacromolecules_U.jpg   03_UN52bMacromolecules_L.jpg

03_UN52bMacromolecules_U.jpg   03_UN52cMacromolecules_L.jpg   03_UN52cMacromolecules_U.jpg   03_UN52dMacromolecules_L.jpg

03_UN52dMacromolecules_U.jpg   03_UN52DNAstructure_L.jpg   03_UN52DNAstructure_U.jpg

Chapter 4 A Tour of the Cell

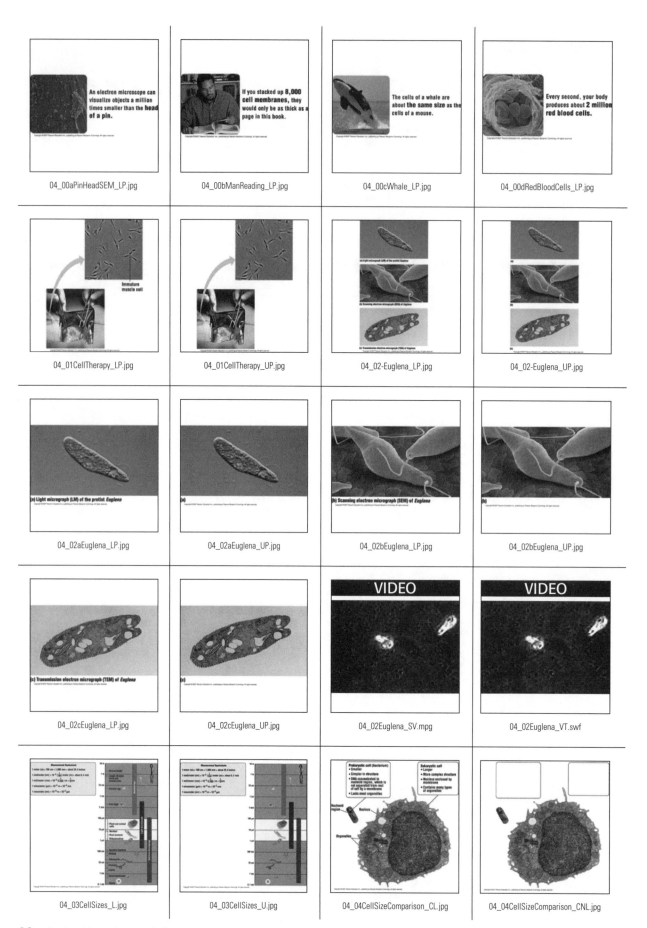

04_00aPinHeadSEM_LP.jpg

04_00bManReading_LP.jpg

04_00cWhale_LP.jpg

04_00dRedBloodCells_LP.jpg

04_01CellTherapy_LP.jpg

04_01CellTherapy_UP.jpg

04_02-Euglena_LP.jpg

04_02-Euglena_UP.jpg

04_02aEuglena_LP.jpg

04_02aEuglena_UP.jpg

04_02bEuglena_LP.jpg

04_02bEuglena_UP.jpg

04_02cEuglena_LP.jpg

04_02cEuglena_UP.jpg

04_02Euglena_SV.mpg

04_02Euglena_VT.swf

04_03CellSizes_L.jpg

04_03CellSizes_U.jpg

04_04CellSizeComparison_CL.jpg

04_04CellSizeComparison_CNL.jpg

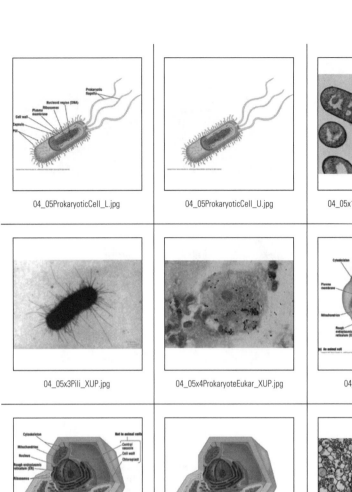

04_05ProkaryoticCell_L.jpg

04_05ProkaryoticCell_U.jpg

04_05x1BacillusPolymyxa_XUP.jpg

04_05x2Ecoli_XUP.jpg

04_05x3Pili_XUP.jpg

04_05x4ProkaryoteEukar_XUP.jpg

04_06aAnimalCell_L.jpg

04_06aAnimalCell_U.jpg

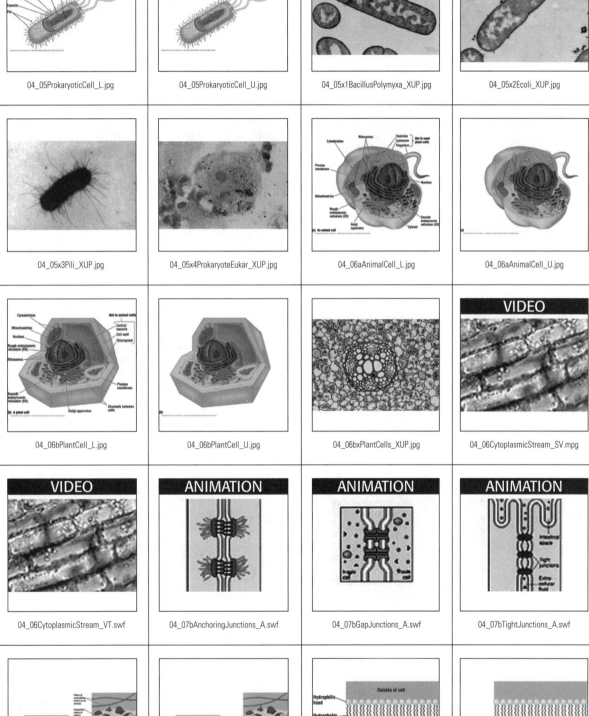

04_06bPlantCell_L.jpg

04_06bPlantCell_U.jpg

04_06bxPlantCells_XUP.jpg

04_06CytoplasmicStream_SV.mpg

VIDEO

04_06CytoplasmicStream_VT.swf

ANIMATION

04_07bAnchoringJunctions_A.swf

ANIMATION

04_07bGapJunctions_A.swf

ANIMATION

04_07bTightJunctions_A.swf

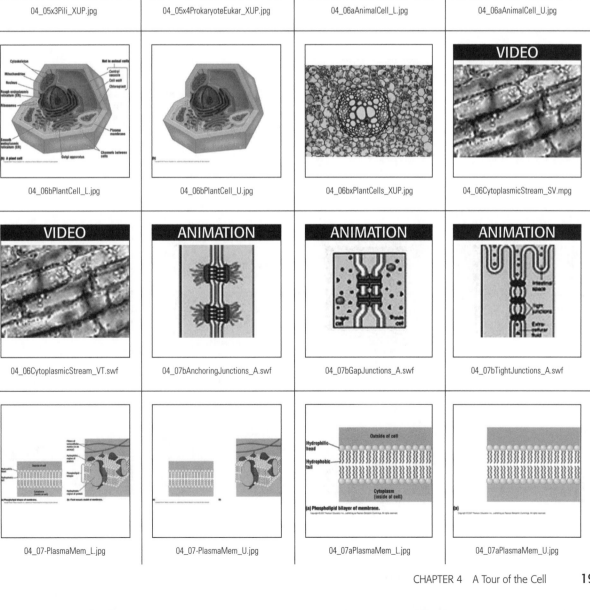

04_07-PlasmaMem_L.jpg

04_07-PlasmaMem_U.jpg

04_07aPlasmaMem_L.jpg

04_07aPlasmaMem_U.jpg

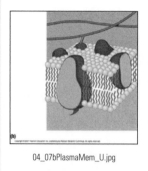

04_07bPlasmaMem_L.jpg

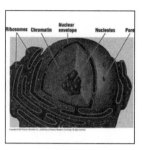

04_07bPlasmaMem_U.jpg

04_08Nucleus_L.jpg

04_08Nucleus_U.jpg

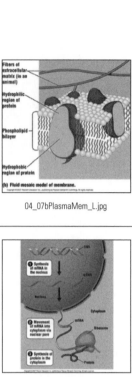

04_09DNARNAProtein_L.jpg

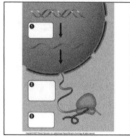

04_09DNARNAProtein_U.jpg

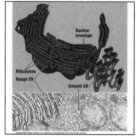

04_10ER_CL.jpg

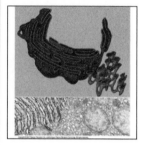

04_10ER_CNL.jpg

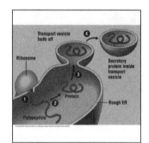

04_11RoughER_L.jpg

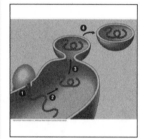

04_11RoughER_U.jpg

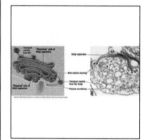

04_12GolgiApparatus_CL.jpg

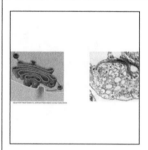

04_12GolgiApparatus_CNL.jpg

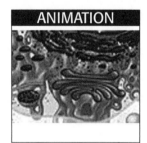

ANIMATION

04_13LysosomeFormation_A.swf

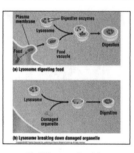

04_13-LysosomeFxn_L.jpg

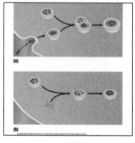

04_13-LysosomeFxn_U.jpg

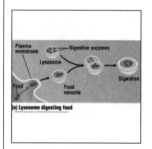

04_13aLysosomeFxn_L.jpg

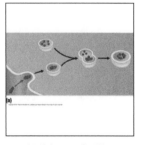

04_13aLysosomeFxn_U.jpg

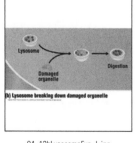

04_13bLysosomeFxn_L.jpg

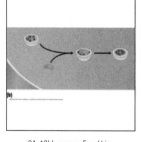

04_13bLysosomeFxn_U.jpg

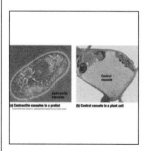

04_14-Vacuoles_LP.jpg

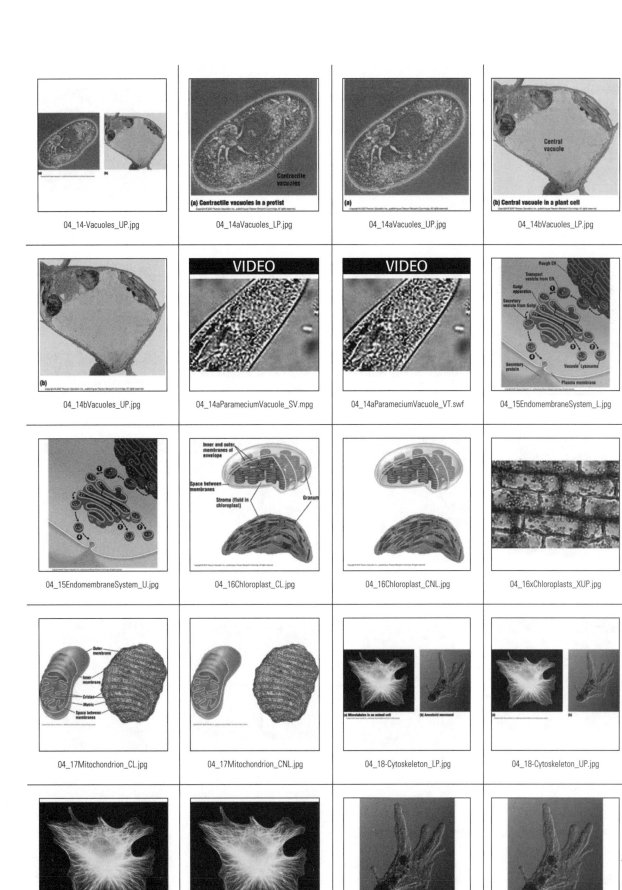

04_14-Vacuoles_UP.jpg

04_14aVacuoles_LP.jpg

04_14aVacuoles_UP.jpg

04_14bVacuoles_LP.jpg

04_14bVacuoles_UP.jpg

04_14aParameciumVacuole_SV.mpg

04_14aParameciumVacuole_VT.swf

04_15EndomembraneSystem_L.jpg

04_15EndomembraneSystem_U.jpg

04_16Chloroplast_CL.jpg

04_16Chloroplast_CNL.jpg

04_16xChloroplasts_XUP.jpg

04_17Mitochondrion_CL.jpg

04_17Mitochondrion_CNL.jpg

04_18-Cytoskeleton_LP.jpg

04_18-Cytoskeleton_UP.jpg

04_18aCytoskeleton_LP.jpg

04_18aCytoskeleton_UP.jpg

04_18bCytoskeleton_LP.jpg

04_18bCytoskeleton_UP.jpg

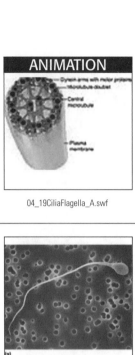

ANIMATION

04_19CiliaFlagella_A.swf

04_19-FlagellaCilia_LP.jpg

04_19-FlagellaCilia_UP.jpg

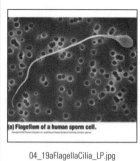

04_19aFlagellaCilia_LP.jpg

04_19aFlagellaCilia_UP.jpg

04_19bFlagellaCilia_LP.jpg

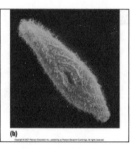

04_19bFlagellaCilia_UP.jpg

04_19cFlagellaCilia_LP.jpg

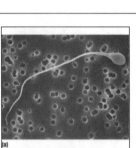

04_19cFlagellaCilia_UP.jpg

VIDEO

04_19aChlamydomonas_SV.mpg

VIDEO

04_19aChlamydomonas_VT.swf

VIDEO

04_19bParameciumCilia_SV.mpg

VIDEO

04_19bParameciumCilia_VT.swf

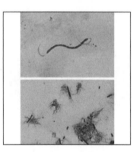

04_19xFlagella_XUP.jpg

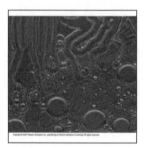

04_20MembraneSelfAssembl_U.jpg

04_20xPhospholipidSpher_XUP.jpg

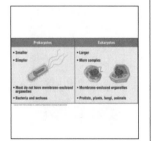

04_UN70aProkarVsEukary_L.jpg

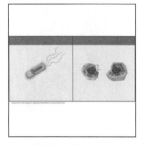

04_UN70aProkarVsEukary_U.jpg

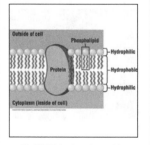

04_UN70bMembraneStruct_L.jpg

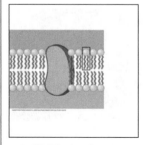

04_UN70bMembraneStruct_U.jpg

Chapter 5 The Working Cell

05_00aPizza_LP.jpg

05_00bPeanuts_LP.jpg

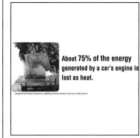
05_00cAthelete_LP.jpg

05_00dOverheatingCar_LP.jpg

05_01BlueJeans_UP.jpg

05_02EnergyConcepts_A.swf

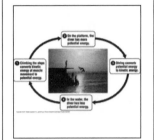
05_02EnergyConversions_CL.jpg

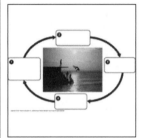
05_02EnergyConversions_CNL.jpg

05_02x1KEslide_XUP.jpg

05_02x2PEandKEcheetah_XUP.jpg

05_02x3PEandKEdam_XUP.jpg

05_03-EnergyConversions_L.jpg

05_03-EnergyConversions_U.jpg

05_03aEnergyConversions_L.jpg

05_03aEnergyConversions_U.jpg

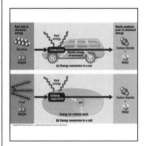
05_03bEnergyConversions_L.jpg

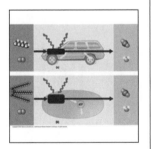
05_03bEnergyConversions_U.jpg

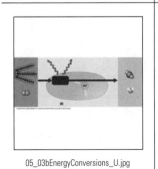
05_04aCalories_L.jpg

05_04aCalories_U.jpg

05_04bCalories_L.jpg

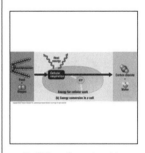

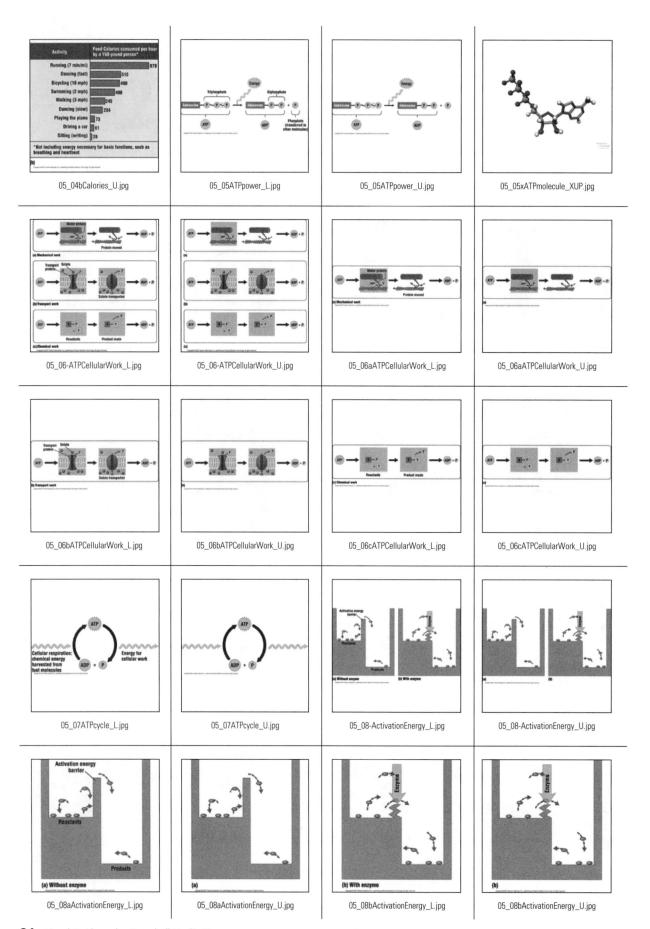

05_04bCalories_U.jpg

05_05ATPpower_L.jpg

05_05ATPpower_U.jpg

05_05xATPmolecule_XUP.jpg

05_06-ATPCellularWork_L.jpg

05_06-ATPCellularWork_U.jpg

05_06aATPCellularWork_L.jpg

05_06aATPCellularWork_U.jpg

05_06bATPCellularWork_L.jpg

05_06bATPCellularWork_U.jpg

05_06cATPCellularWork_L.jpg

05_06cATPCellularWork_U.jpg

05_07ATPcycle_L.jpg

05_07ATPcycle_U.jpg

05_08-ActivationEnergy_L.jpg

05_08-ActivationEnergy_U.jpg

05_08aActivationEnergy_L.jpg

05_08aActivationEnergy_U.jpg

05_08bActivationEnergy_L.jpg

05_08bActivationEnergy_U.jpg

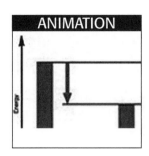

05_09HowEnzymesWork_A.swf

05_09EnzymeWorks_1_L.jpg

05_09EnzymeWorks_1_U.jpg

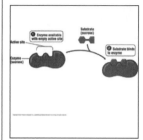

05_09EnzymeWorks_2_L.jpg

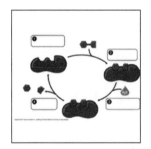

05_09EnzymeWorks_2_U.jpg

05_09EnzymeWorks_3_L.jpg

05_09EnzymeWorks_3_U.jpg

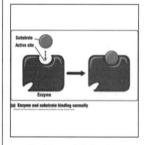

05_09EnzymeWorks_4_L.jpg

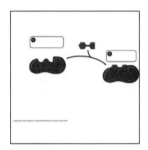

05_09EnzymeWorks_4_U.jpg

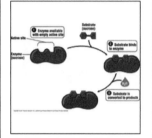

05_10-EnzymeInhibition_L.jpg

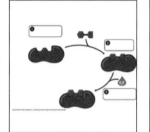

05_10-EnzymeInhibition_U.jpg

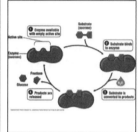

05_10aEnzymeInhibition_L.jpg

05_10aEnzymeInhibition_U.jpg

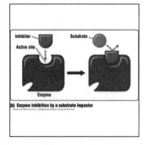

05_10bEnzymeInhibition_L.jpg

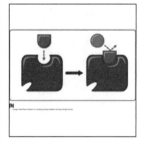

05_10bEnzymeInhibition_U.jpg

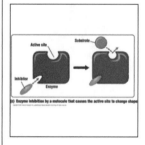

05_10cEnzymeInhibition_L.jpg

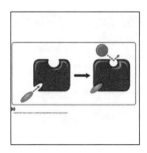

05_10cEnzymeInhibition_U.jpg

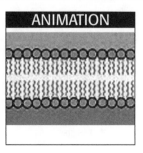

05_11MembraneSelectivity_A.swf

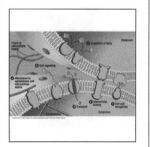

05_11MembrProteinFunc_L.jpg

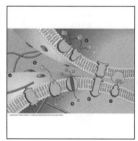

05_11MembrProteinFunc_U.jpg

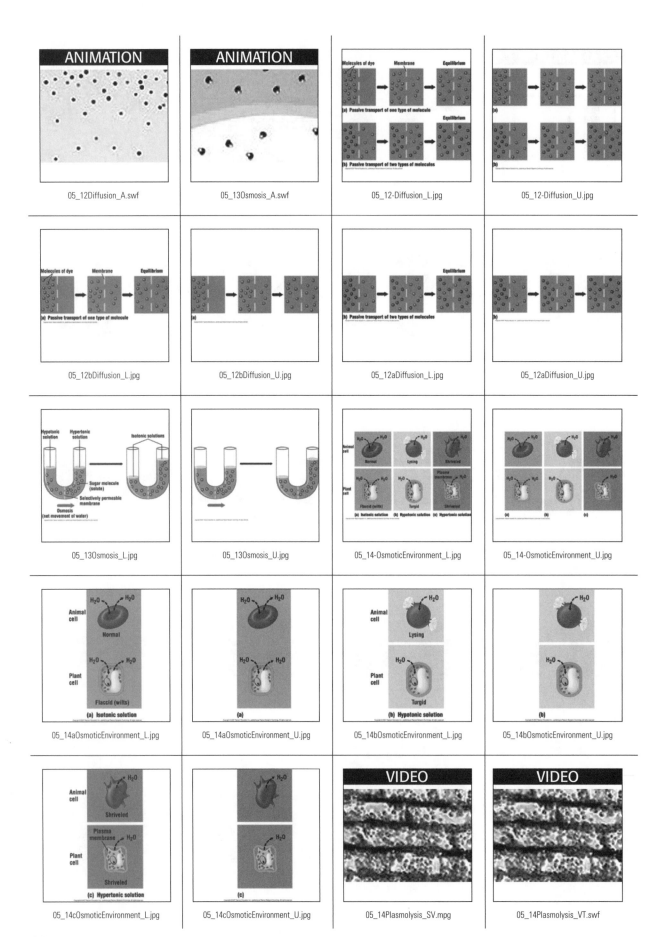

ANIMATION

05_12Diffusion_A.swf

ANIMATION

05_13Osmosis_A.swf

05_12-Diffusion_L.jpg

05_12-Diffusion_U.jpg

05_12bDiffusion_L.jpg

05_12bDiffusion_U.jpg

05_12aDiffusion_L.jpg

05_12aDiffusion_U.jpg

05_13Osmosis_L.jpg

05_13Osmosis_U.jpg

05_14-OsmoticEnvironment_L.jpg

05_14-OsmoticEnvironment_U.jpg

05_14aOsmoticEnvironment_L.jpg

05_14aOsmoticEnvironment_U.jpg

05_14bOsmoticEnvironment_L.jpg

05_14bOsmoticEnvironment_U.jpg

05_14cOsmoticEnvironment_L.jpg

05_14cOsmoticEnvironment_U.jpg

VIDEO

05_14Plasmolysis_SV.mpg

VIDEO

05_14Plasmolysis_VT.swf

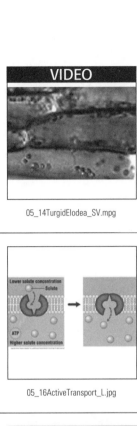

VIDEO

05_14TurgidElodea_SV.mpg

VIDEO

05_14TurgidElodea_VT.swf

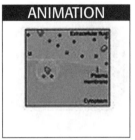

05_15PlantTurgor_UP.jpg

ANIMATION

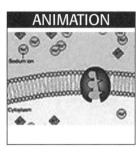

05_16ActiveTransport_A.swf

05_16ActiveTransport_L.jpg

05_16ActiveTransport_U.jpg

ANIMATION

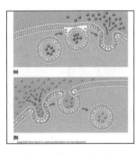

05_17ExocytEndoIntro_A.swf

ANIMATION

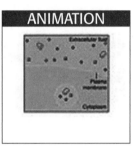

05_17aExocytosis_A.swf

ANIMATION

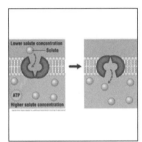

05_17bPinocytosis_A.swf

05_17-ExoEndocytosis_L.jpg

05_17-ExoEndocytosis_U.jpg

05_17aExocytosis_L.jpg

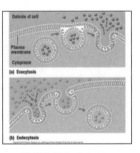

05_17aExocytosis_U.jpg

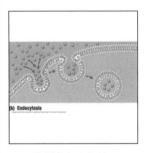

05_17bEndocytosis_L.jpg

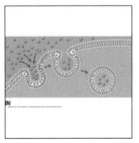

05_17bEndocytosis_U.jpg

ANIMATION

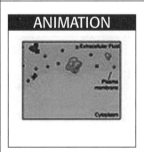

05_18Phagocytosis_A.swf

05_18Phagocytosis_LP.jpg

05_18Phagocytosis_UP.jpg

ANIMATION

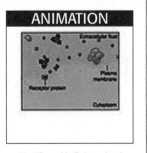

05_19ReceptMedEndocyt_A.swf

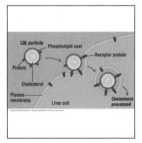

05_19CholesterolUptake_L.jpg

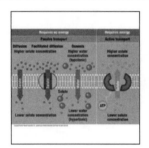

05_19CholesterolUptake_U.jpg

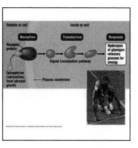

05_20-CellSignaling_CL.jpg

05_20-CellSignaling_CNL.jpg

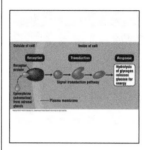

05_20aCellSignaling_L.jpg

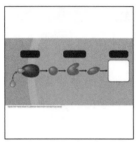

05_20aCellSignaling_U.jpg

05_21EnzymeLactase_L.jpg

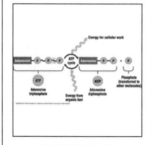

05_UN85ATPCycle_L.jpg

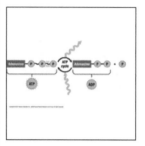

05_UN85ATPCycle_U.jpg

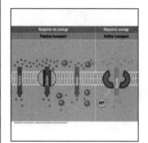

05_UN86aMembStructure_L.jpg

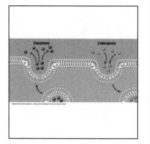

05_UN86aMembStructure_U.jpg

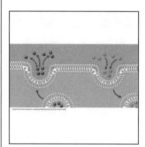

05_UN86bEndoExocytosis_L.jpg

05_UN86bEndoExocytosis_U.jpg

Chapter 6 Cellular Respiration: Obtaining Energy from Food

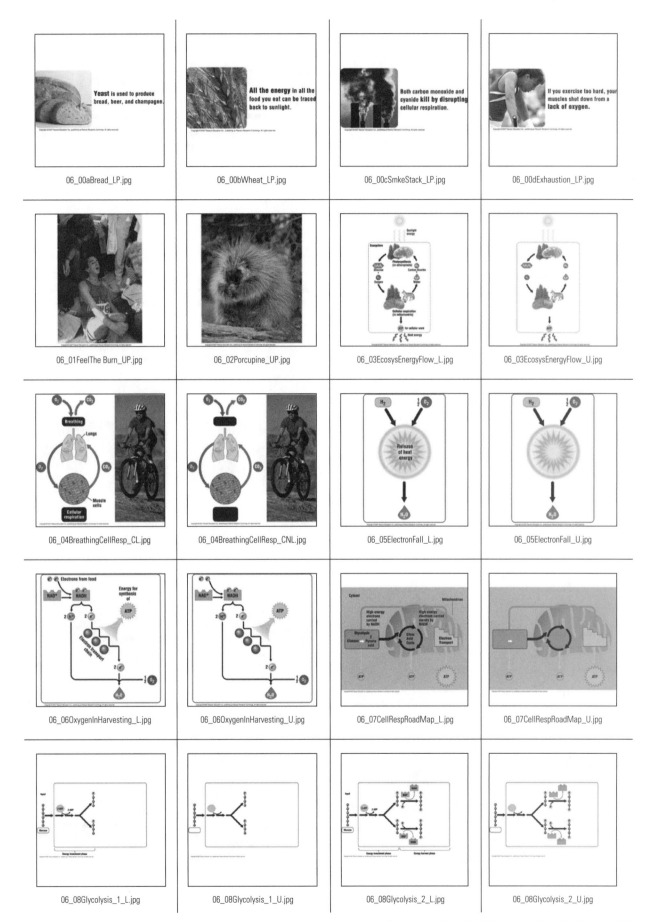

06_00aBread_LP.jpg

06_00bWheat_LP.jpg

06_00cSmkeStack_LP.jpg

06_00dExhaustion_LP.jpg

06_01FeelThe Burn_UP.jpg

06_02Porcupine_UP.jpg

06_03EcosysEnergyFlow_L.jpg

06_03EcosysEnergyFlow_U.jpg

06_04BreathingCellResp_CL.jpg

06_04BreathingCellResp_CNL.jpg

06_05ElectronFall_L.jpg

06_05ElectronFall_U.jpg

06_06OxygenInHarvesting_L.jpg

06_06OxygenInHarvesting_U.jpg

06_07CellRespRoadMap_L.jpg

06_07CellRespRoadMap_U.jpg

06_08Glycolysis_1_L.jpg

06_08Glycolysis_1_U.jpg

06_08Glycolysis_2_L.jpg

06_08Glycolysis_2_U.jpg

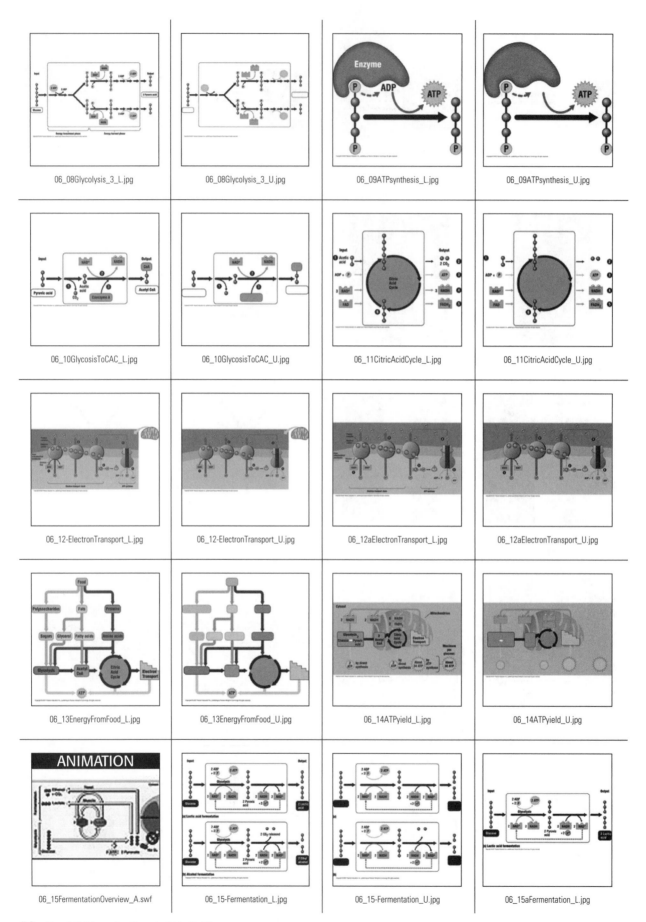

06_08Glycolysis_3_L.jpg

06_08Glycolysis_3_U.jpg

06_09ATPsynthesis_L.jpg

06_09ATPsynthesis_U.jpg

06_10GlycosisToCAC_L.jpg

06_10GlycosisToCAC_U.jpg

06_11CitricAcidCycle_L.jpg

06_11CitricAcidCycle_U.jpg

06_12-ElectronTransport_L.jpg

06_12-ElectronTransport_U.jpg

06_12aElectronTransport_L.jpg

06_12aElectronTransport_U.jpg

06_13EnergyFromFood_L.jpg

06_13EnergyFromFood_U.jpg

06_14ATPyield_L.jpg

06_14ATPyield_U.jpg

06_15FermentationOverview_A.swf

06_15-Fermentation_L.jpg

06_15-Fermentation_U.jpg

06_15aFermentation_L.jpg

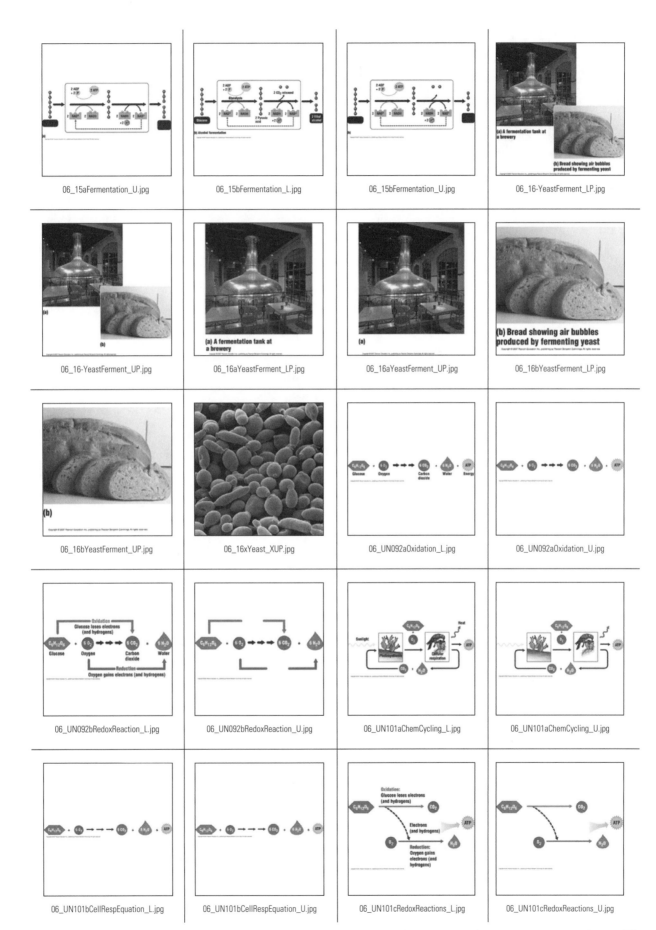

06_15aFermentation_U.jpg

06_15bFermentation_L.jpg

06_15bFermentation_U.jpg

06_16-YeastFerment_LP.jpg

06_16-YeastFerment_UP.jpg

06_16aYeastFerment_LP.jpg

06_16aYeastFerment_UP.jpg

06_16bYeastFerment_LP.jpg

06_16bYeastFerment_UP.jpg

06_16xYeast_XUP.jpg

06_UN092aOxidation_L.jpg

06_UN092aOxidation_U.jpg

06_UN092bRedoxReaction_L.jpg

06_UN092bRedoxReaction_U.jpg

06_UN101aChemCycling_L.jpg

06_UN101aChemCycling_U.jpg

06_UN101bCellRespEquation_L.jpg

06_UN101bCellRespEquation_U.jpg

06_UN101cRedoxReactions_L.jpg

06_UN101cRedoxReactions_U.jpg

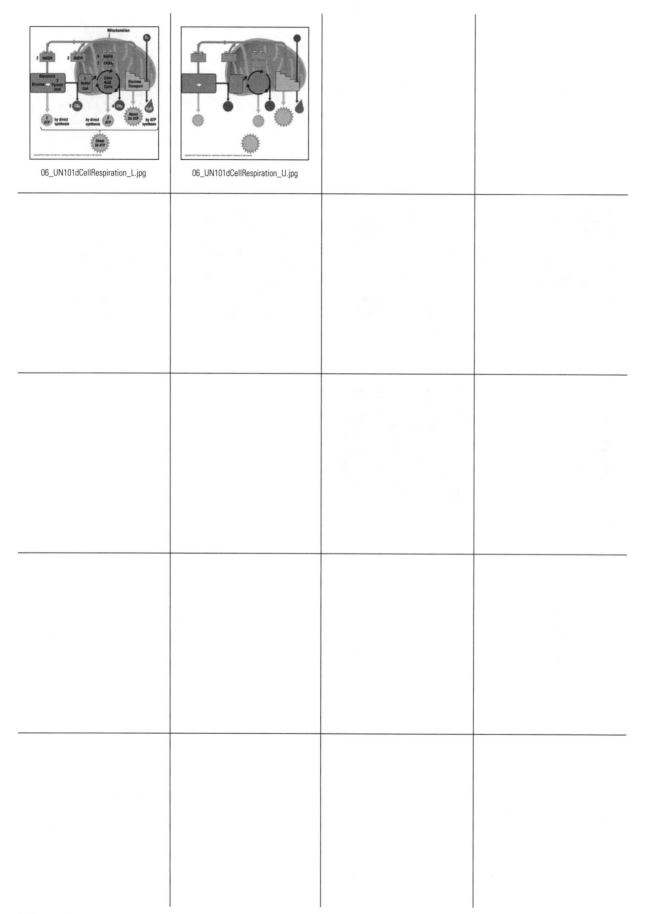

06_UN101dCellRespiration_L.jpg

06_UN101dCellRespiration_U.jpg

Chapter 7 Photosynthesis: Using Light to Make Food

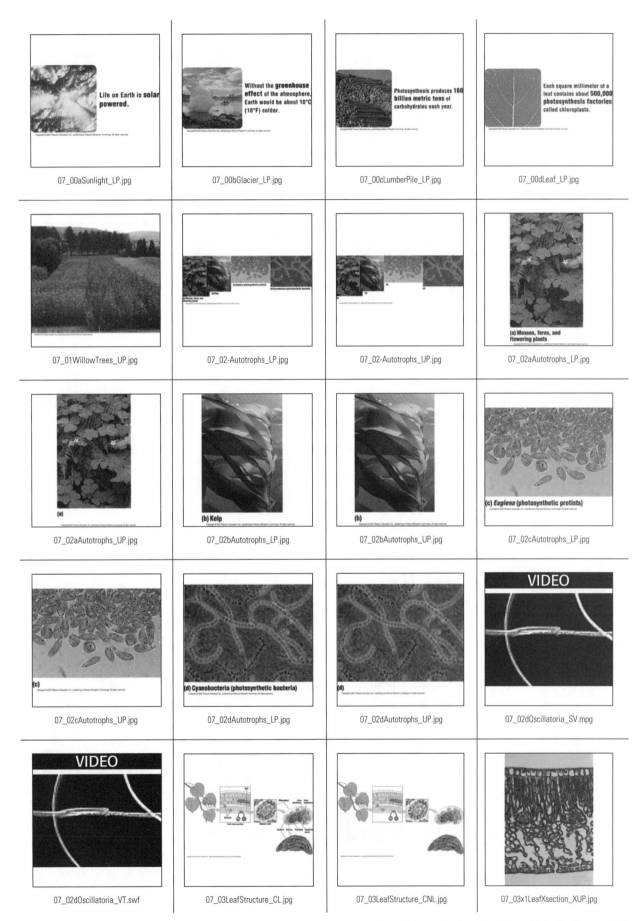

07_00aSunlight_LP.jpg

07_00bGlacier_LP.jpg

07_00cLumberPile_LP.jpg

07_00dLeaf_LP.jpg

07_01WillowTrees_UP.jpg

07_02-Autotrophs_LP.jpg

07_02-Autotrophs_UP.jpg

07_02aAutotrophs_LP.jpg

07_02aAutotrophs_UP.jpg

07_02bAutotrophs_LP.jpg

07_02bAutotrophs_UP.jpg

07_02cAutotrophs_LP.jpg

07_02cAutotrophs_UP.jpg

07_02dAutotrophs_LP.jpg

07_02dAutotrophs_UP.jpg

07_02dOscillatoria_SV.mpg

07_02dOscillatoria_VT.swf

07_03LeafStructure_CL.jpg

07_03LeafStructure_CNL.jpg

07_03x1LeafXsection_XUP.jpg

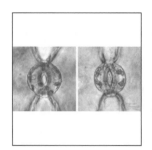

07_03x2StomaOpenClosed_XUP.jpg

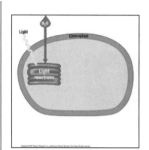

07_04Photosynthesis_1_L.jpg

07_04Photosynthesis_1_U.jpg

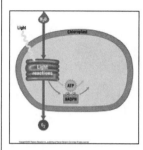

07_04Photosynthesis_2_L.jpg

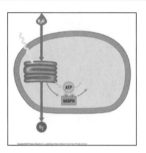

07_04Photosynthesis_2_U.jpg

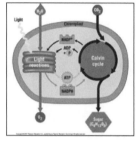

07_04Photosynthesis_3_L.jpg

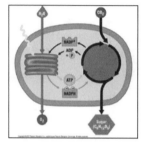

07_04Photosynthesis_3_U.jpg

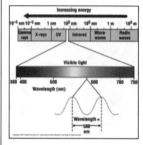

07_05ElectromagSpectrum_L.jpg

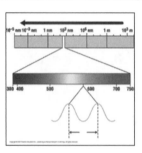

07_05ElectromagSpectrum_U.jpg

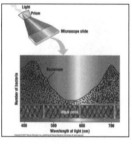

07_06LightWavelengths_L.jpg

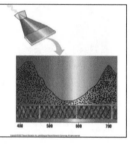

07_06LightWavelengths_U.jpg

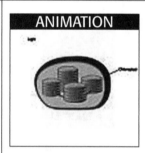

07_07LightAndPigments_A.swf

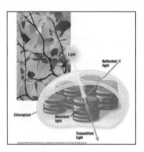

07_07ReflectionOfGreen_CL.jpg

07_07ReflectionOfGreen_CNL.jpg

07_08FallFoliage_UP.jpg

07_08xChlorophyllModel_XUP.jpg

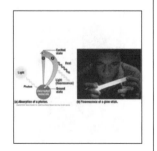

07_09-Electrons_CL.jpg

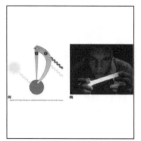

07_09-Electrons_CNL.jpg

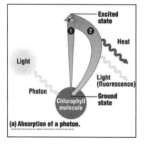

07_09aPhoton_L.jpg

07_09aPhoton_U.jpg

07_09bGlowstick_LP.jpg

07_09bGlowstick_UP.jpg

07_10Photosystem_L.jpg

07_10Photosystem_U.jpg

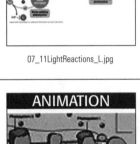

07_11LightReactions_L.jpg

07_11LightReactions_U.jpg

07_12LightReactAnalogy_L.jpg

07_12LightReactAnalogy_U.jpg

07_13LightReactions_A.swf

07_13-ThylakoidMembrane_L.jpg

07_13-ThylakoidMembrane_U.jpg

07_13aThylakoidMembrane_L.jpg

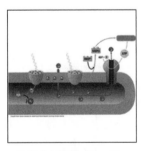

07_13aThylakoidMembrane_U.jpg

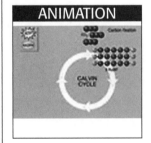

07_14CalvinCycle_1_L.jpg

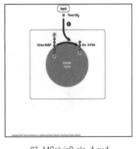

07_14CalvinCycle_A.swf

07_14CalvinCycle_1_U.jpg

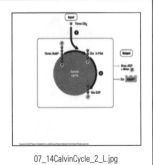

07_14CalvinCycle_2_L.jpg

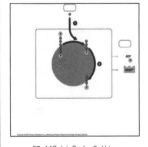

07_14CalvinCycle_2_U.jpg

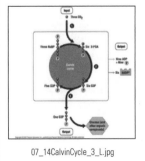

07_14CalvinCycle_3_L.jpg

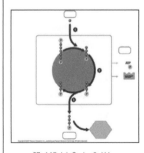

07_14CalvinCycle_3_U.jpg

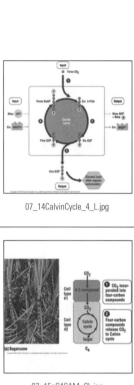

07_14CalvinCycle_4_L.jpg

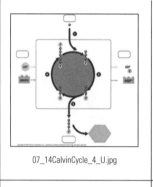

07_14CalvinCycle_4_U.jpg

07_15-C4CAM_CL.jpg

07_15-C4CAM_CNL.jpg

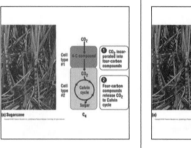

07_15aC4CAM_CL.jpg

07_15aC4CAM_CNL.jpg

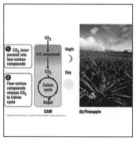

07_15bC4CAM_CL.jpg

07_15bC4CAM_CNL.jpg

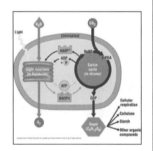

07_16Photosynthesis_L.jpg

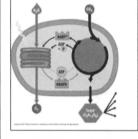

07_16Photosynthesis_U.jpg

07_17Greenhouse_UP.jpg

07_18GlobalWarming_L.jpg

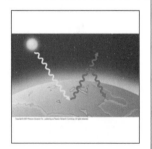

07_18GlobalWarming_U.jpg

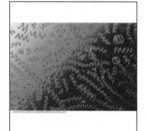

07_19Cyanobacteria_U.jpg

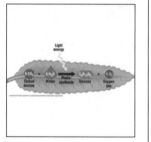

07_UN106Photosynthesis_L.jpg

07_UN106Photosynthesis_U.jpg

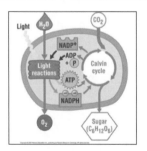

07_UN107LightReactions_L.jpg

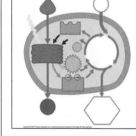

07_UN107LightReactions_U.jpg

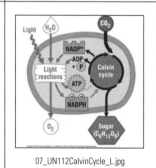

07_UN112CalvinCycle_L.jpg

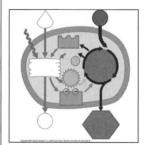

07_UN112CalvinCycle_U.jpg

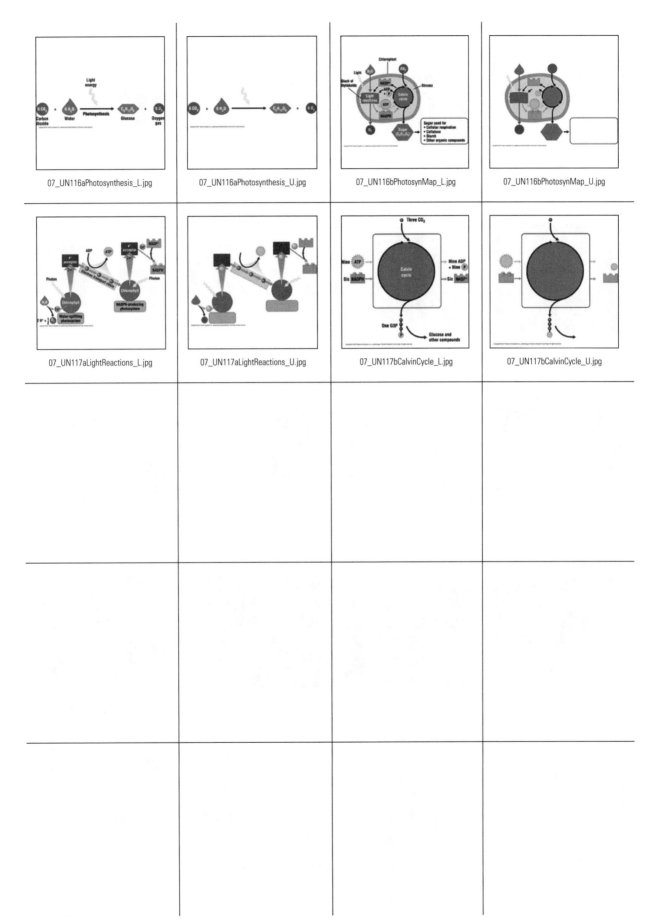

07_UN116aPhotosynthesis_L.jpg

07_UN116aPhotosynthesis_U.jpg

07_UN116bPhotosynMap_L.jpg

07_UN116bPhotosynMap_U.jpg

07_UN117aLightReactions_L.jpg

07_UN117aLightReactions_U.jpg

07_UN117bCalvinCycle_L.jpg

07_UN117bCalvinCycle_U.jpg

Chapter 8 Cellular Reproduction: Cells from Cells

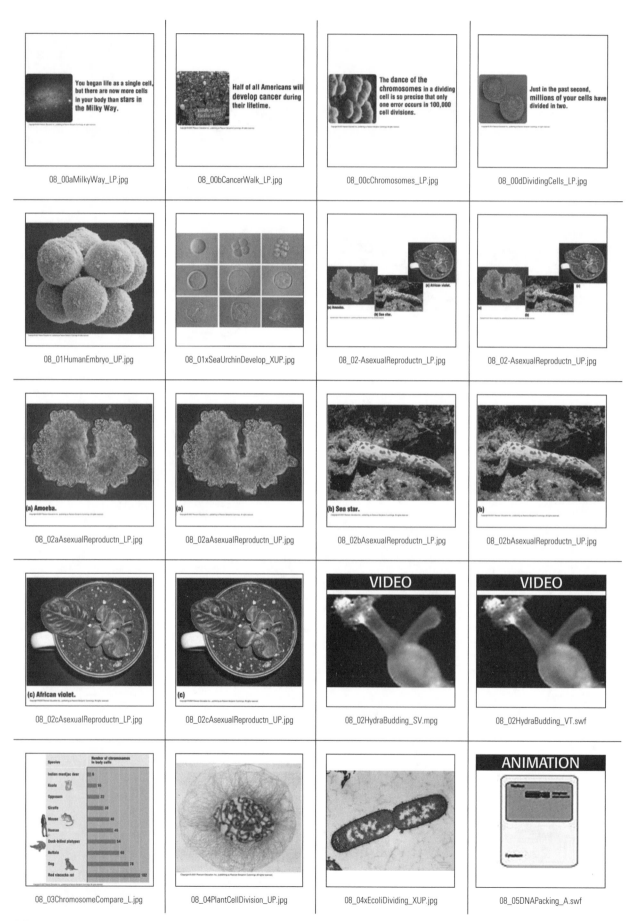

You began life as a single cell, but there are now more cells in your body than stars in the Milky Way.

08_00aMilkyWay_LP.jpg

Half of all Americans will develop cancer during their lifetime.

08_00bCancerWalk_LP.jpg

The dance of the chromosomes in a dividing cell is so precise that only one error occurs in 100,000 cell divisions.

08_00cChromosomes_LP.jpg

Just in the past second, millions of your cells have divided in two.

08_00dDividingCells_LP.jpg

08_01HumanEmbryo_UP.jpg

08_01xSeaUrchinDevelop_XUP.jpg

08_02-AsexualReproductn_LP.jpg

08_02-AsexualReproductn_UP.jpg

(a) Amoeba.

08_02aAsexualReproductn_LP.jpg

(a)

08_02aAsexualReproductn_UP.jpg

(b) Sea star.

08_02bAsexualReproductn_LP.jpg

(b)

08_02bAsexualReproductn_UP.jpg

(c) African violet.

08_02cAsexualReproductn_LP.jpg

(c)

08_02cAsexualReproductn_UP.jpg

VIDEO

08_02HydraBudding_SV.mpg

VIDEO

08_02HydraBudding_VT.swf

08_03ChromosomeCompare_L.jpg

08_04PlantCellDivision_UP.jpg

08_04xEcoliDividing_XUP.jpg

ANIMATION

08_05DNAPacking_A.swf

08_05DNApacking_CL.jpg

08_05DNApacking_CNL.jpg

08_06bMitosisOverview_A.swf

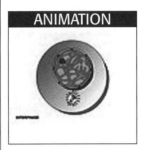

08_06cLateInterphase_A.swf

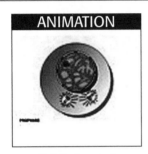

08_06dProphase_A.swf

08_06ePrometaphase_A.swf

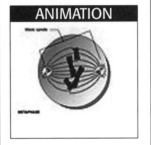

08_06fMetaphase_A.swf

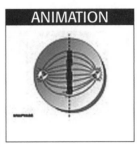

08_06gAnaphase_A.swf

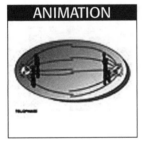

08_06hTelophase_A.swf

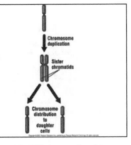

08_06ChromosomeDup_L.jpg

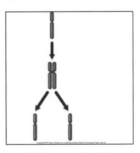

08_06ChromosomeDup_U.jpg

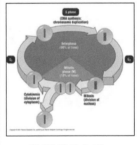

08_07EukCellCycle_L.jpg

08_07EukCellCycle_U.jpg

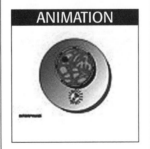

08_07xCellCyleCollage_XUP.jpg

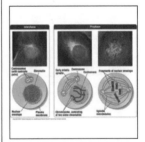

08_08aMitosisAllPhases_A.swf

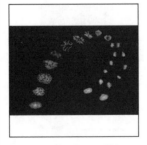

08_08aInterphasProphas_CL.jpg

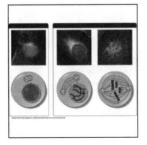

08_08aInterphasProphas_CNL.jpg

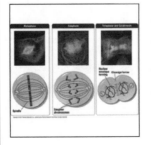

08_08bMetaAnaTeloCyto_CL.jpg

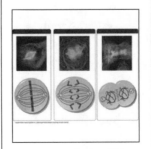

08_08bMetaAnaTeloCyto_CNL.jpg

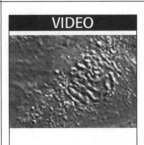

08_08AnimalMitosis_SV.mpg

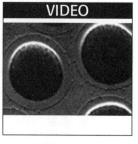

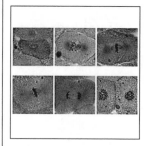

08_08AnimalMitosis_VT.swf

08_08SeaUrchinTimeLapse_SV.mpg

08_08SeaUrchinTimeLapse_VT.swf

08_08x1-MitosisCollage_XUP.jpg

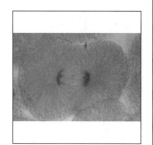

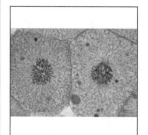

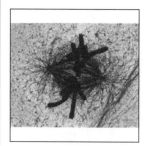

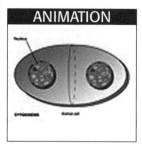

08_08x1aInterphase_XUP.jpg

08_08x1bEarlyProphase_XUP.jpg

08_08x1cLateProphase_XUP.jpg

08_08x1dMetaphase_XUP.jpg

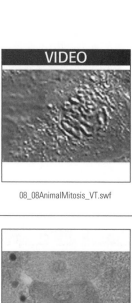

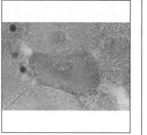

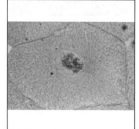

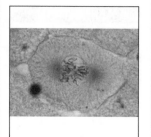

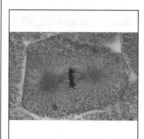

08_08x1eAnaphase_XUP.jpg

08_08x1fLateTelophase_XUP.jpg

08_08x2MitoticSpindle_XUP.jpg

08_09Cytokinesis_A.swf

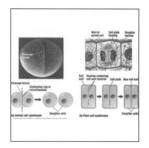

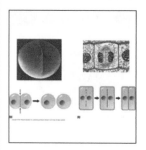

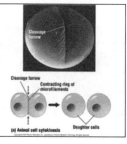

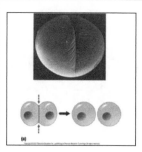

08_09-Cytokinesis_CL.jpg

08_09-Cytokinesis_CNL.jpg

08_09aCytokinesis_CL.jpg

08_09aCytokinesis_CNL.jpg

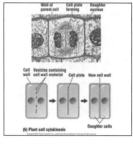

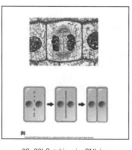

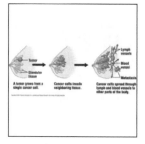

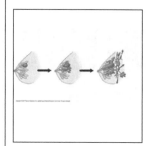

08_09bCytokinesis_CL.jpg

08_09bCytokinesis_CNL.jpg

08_10CancerMetastasis_L.jpg

08_10CancerMetastasis_U.jpg

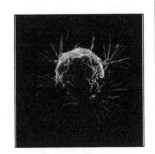

08_10x1BreastCancerCell_XUP.jpg

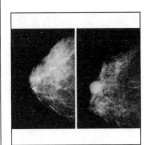

08_10x2-MammogrmNrmlCan_XUP.jpg

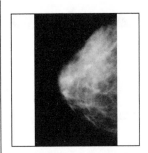

08_10x2aMammogramNormal_XUP.jpg

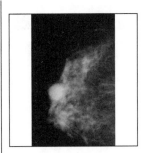

08_10x2bMammogramCancer_XUP.jpg

08_10x3FibroblastGrowth_XUP.jpg

08_11LabCancerCells_UP.jpg

08_12ReproVariation_UP.jpg

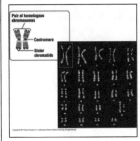

08_13NormalKaryotype_L.jpg

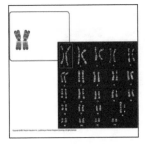

08_13NormalKaryotype_U.jpg

08_13x1HumanFemaleChrom_XLP.jpg

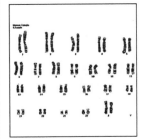

08_13x2HumanFemaleKaryo_XLP.jpg

08_13x3HumanMaleChromo_XLP.jpg

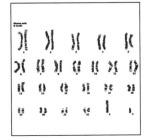

08_13x4HumanMaleKaryo_XLP.jpg

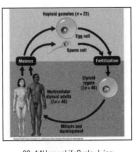

08_14HumanLifeCycle_L.jpg

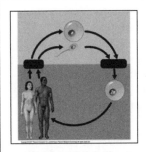

08_14HumanLifeCycle_U.jpg

08_15MeiosisHalvesChromo_L.jpg

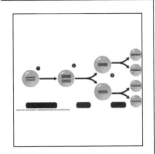

08_15MeiosisHalvesChromo_U.jpg

ANIMATION

08_16aMeiosisOverview_A.swf

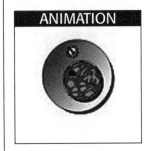

ANIMATION

08_16bInterphase_A.swf

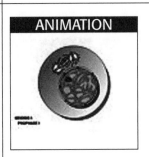

ANIMATION

08_16cProphaseI_A.swf

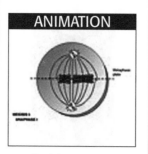
ANIMATION

08_16dMetaphaseI_A.swf

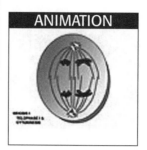
ANIMATION

08_16eAnaphaseI_A.swf

ANIMATION

08_16fTelophaseICytokin_A.swf

ANIMATION

08_16gProphaseII_A.swf

ANIMATION

08_16hMetaphaseII_A.swf

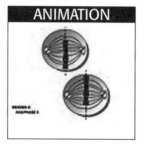
ANIMATION

08_16iAnaphaseII_A.swf

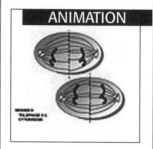
ANIMATION

08_16jTelophaseIICytokin_A.swf

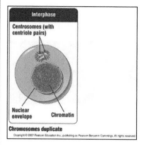
08_16aMeiosisInterphas_L.jpg

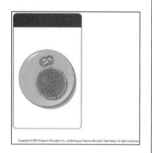
08_16aMeiosisInterphas_U.jpg

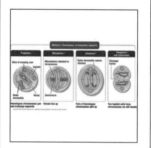
08_16bMeiosisI_L.jpg

08_16bMeiosisI_U.jpg

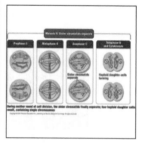
08_16cMeiosisII_L.jpg

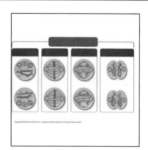
08_16cMeiosisII_U.jpg

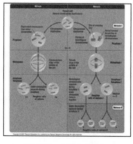
08_17MitosisMeiosis_L.jpg

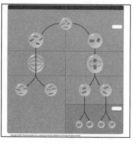
08_17MitosisMeiosis_U.jpg

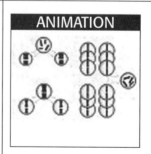
ANIMATION

08_18GeneticVariation_A.swf

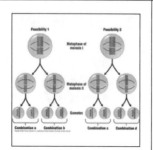
08_18MetaphasVariation_L.jpg

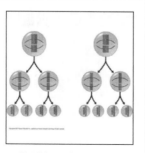
08_18MetaphasVariation_U.jpg

ANIMATION

08_19CrossingOver_A.swf

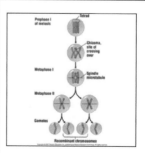
08_19CrossingOver_L.jpg

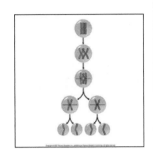

08_19CrossingOver_U.jpg

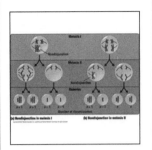

08_20Nondisjunction_L.jpg

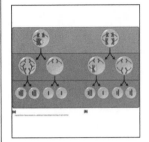

08_20Nondisjunction_U.jpg

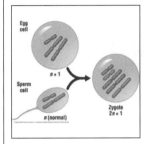

08_21AneuploidyTrisomy_L.jpg

08_21AneuploidyTrisomy_U.jpg

08_22DownSyndromeTrisomy_UP.jpg

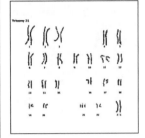

08_22x1DownKaryotypeBW_XLP.jpg

08_22x2KlinefelterKaryo_XLP.jpg

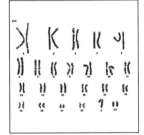

08_22x3XYYkaryotype_XLP.jpg

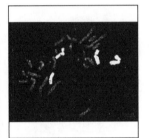

08_22x4TranslocationPho_XUP.jpg

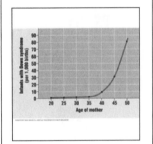

08_23DownMaternalAge_L.jpg

08_24TetraploidRat_UP.jpg

08_T01ChromAbnormalities_T.jpg

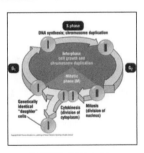

08_UN141aCellCycle_L.jpg

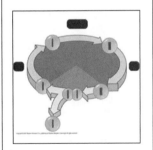

08_UN141aCellCycle_U.jpg

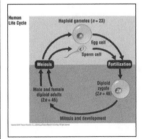

08_UN141bSexCellLifeCycle_L.jpg

08_UN141bSexCellLifeCycle_U.jpg

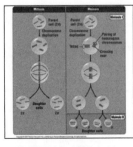

08_UN141cMitosisMeiosis_L.jpg

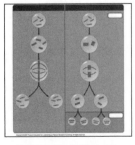

08_UN141cMitosisMeiosis_U.jpg

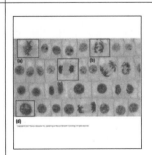

08_UN142OnionTipRoot_UP.jpg

Chapter 9 Patterns of Inheritance

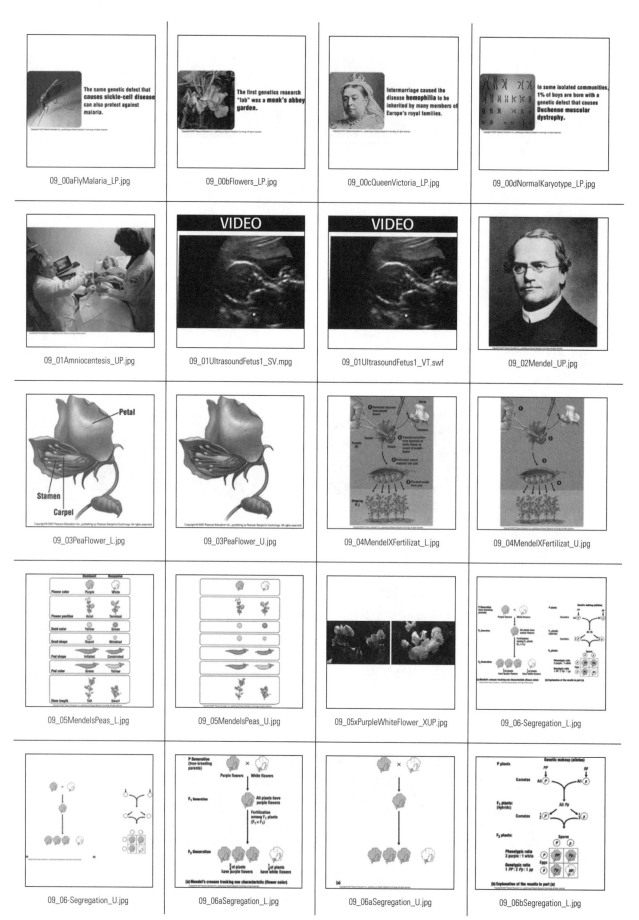

09_00aFlyMalaria_LP.jpg

09_00bFlowers_LP.jpg

09_00cQueenVictoria_LP.jpg

09_00dNormalKaryotype_LP.jpg

09_01Amniocentesis_UP.jpg

09_01UltrasoundFetus1_SV.mpg

09_01UltrasoundFetus1_VT.swf

09_02Mendel_UP.jpg

09_03PeaFlower_L.jpg

09_03PeaFlower_U.jpg

09_04MendelXFertilizat_L.jpg

09_04MendelXFertilizat_U.jpg

09_05MendelsPeas_L.jpg

09_05MendelsPeas_U.jpg

09_05xPurpleWhiteFlower_XUP.jpg

09_06-Segregation_L.jpg

09_06-Segregation_U.jpg

09_06aSegregation_L.jpg

09_06aSegregation_U.jpg

09_06bSegregation_L.jpg

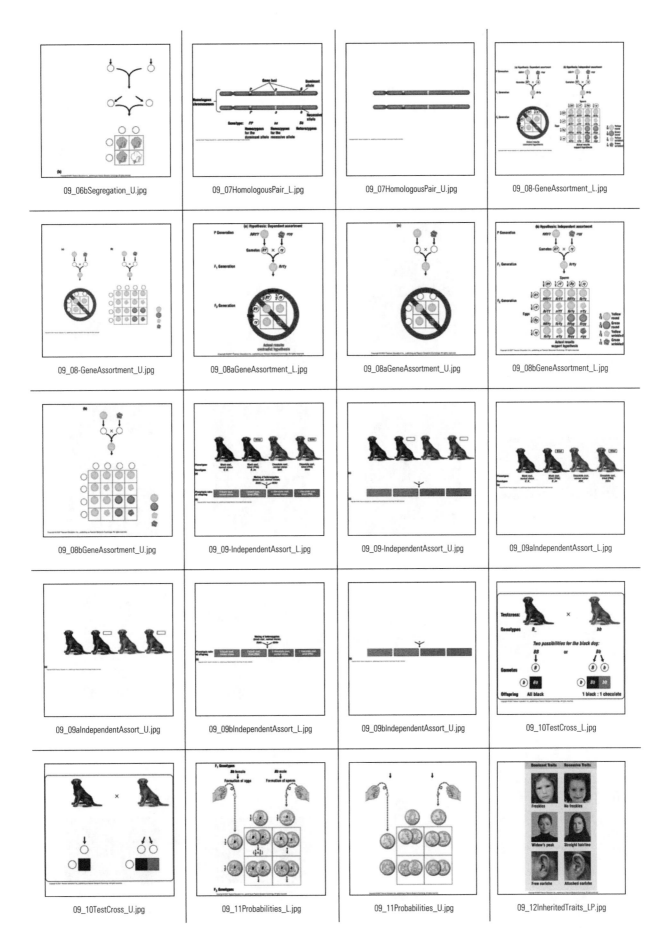

09_06bSegregation_U.jpg

09_07HomologousPair_L.jpg

09_07HomologousPair_U.jpg

09_08-GeneAssortment_L.jpg

09_08-GeneAssortment_U.jpg

09_08aGeneAssortment_L.jpg

09_08aGeneAssortment_U.jpg

09_08bGeneAssortment_L.jpg

09_08bGeneAssortment_U.jpg

09_09-IndependentAssort_L.jpg

09_09-IndependentAssort_U.jpg

09_09aIndependentAssort_L.jpg

09_09aIndependentAssort_U.jpg

09_09bIndependentAssort_L.jpg

09_09bIndependentAssort_U.jpg

09_10TestCross_L.jpg

09_10TestCross_U.jpg

09_11Probabilities_L.jpg

09_11Probabilities_U.jpg

09_12InheritedTraits_LP.jpg

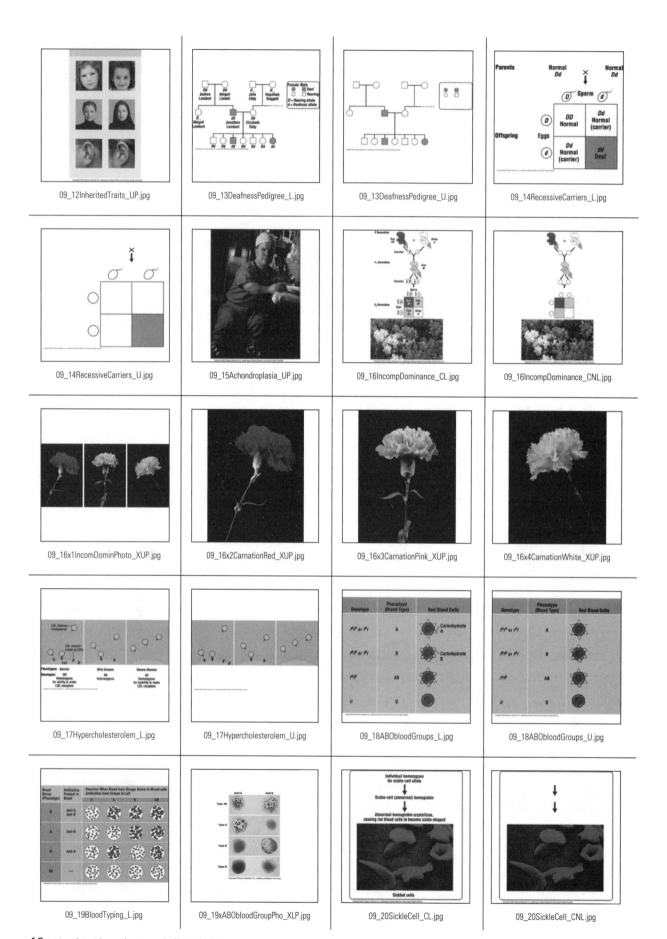

09_12InheritedTraits_UP.jpg

09_13DeafnessPedigree_L.jpg

09_13DeafnessPedigree_U.jpg

09_14RecessiveCarriers_L.jpg

09_14RecessiveCarriers_U.jpg

09_15Achondroplasia_UP.jpg

09_16IncompDominance_CL.jpg

09_16IncompDominance_CNL.jpg

09_16x1IncomDominPhoto_XUP.jpg

09_16x2CarnationRed_XUP.jpg

09_16x3CarnationPink_XUP.jpg

09_16x4CarnationWhite_XUP.jpg

09_17Hypercholesterolem_L.jpg

09_17Hypercholesterolem_U.jpg

09_18ABObloodGroups_L.jpg

09_18ABObloodGroups_U.jpg

09_19BloodTyping_L.jpg

09_19xABObloodGroupPho_XLP.jpg

09_20SickleCell_CL.jpg

09_20SickleCell_CNL.jpg

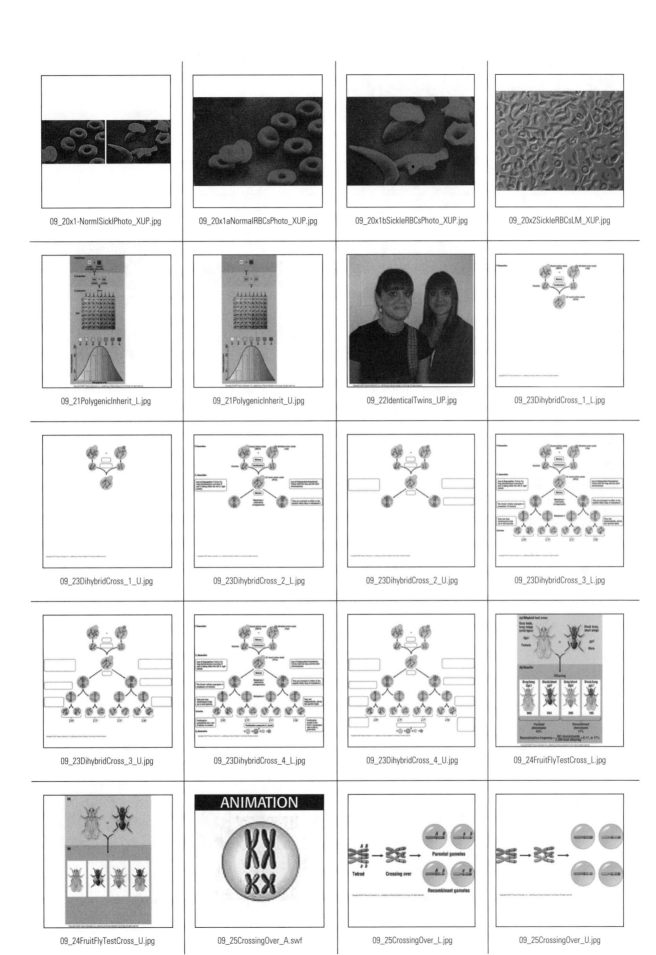

09_20x1-NormlSicklPhoto_XUP.jpg

09_20x1aNormalRBCsPhoto_XUP.jpg

09_20x1bSickleRBCsPhoto_XUP.jpg

09_20x2SickleRBCsLM_XUP.jpg

09_21PolygenicInherit_L.jpg

09_21PolygenicInherit_U.jpg

09_22IdenticalTwins_UP.jpg

09_23DihybridCross_1_L.jpg

09_23DihybridCross_1_U.jpg

09_23DihybridCross_2_L.jpg

09_23DihybridCross_2_U.jpg

09_23DihybridCross_3_L.jpg

09_23DihybridCross_3_U.jpg

09_23DihybridCross_4_L.jpg

09_23DihybridCross_4_U.jpg

09_24FruitFlyTestCross_L.jpg

09_24FruitFlyTestCross_U.jpg

09_25CrossingOver_A.swf

09_25CrossingOver_L.jpg

09_25CrossingOver_U.jpg

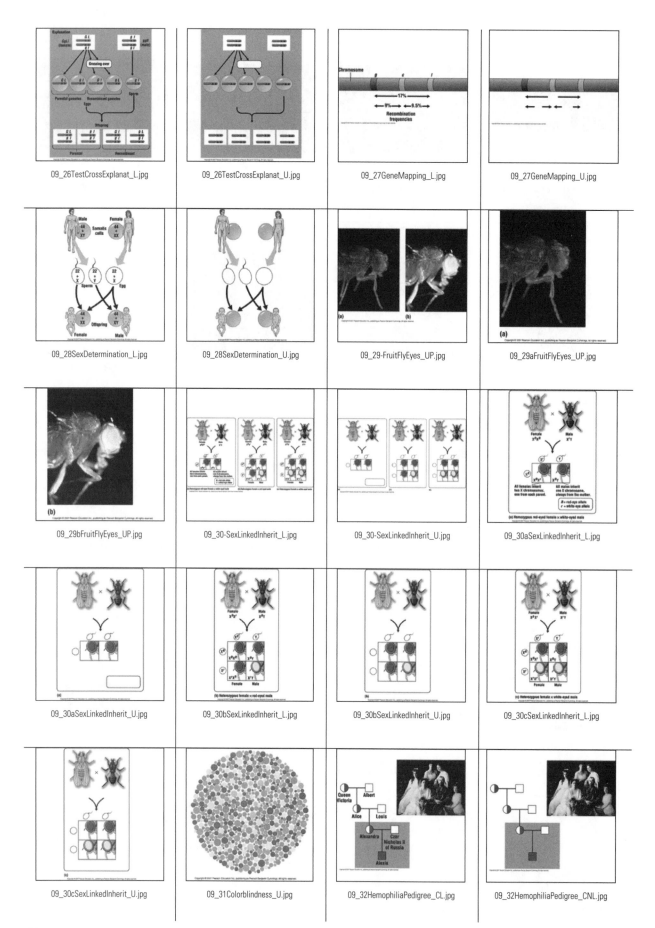

09_26TestCrossExplanat_L.jpg

09_26TestCrossExplanat_U.jpg

09_27GeneMapping_L.jpg

09_27GeneMapping_U.jpg

09_28SexDetermination_L.jpg

09_28SexDetermination_U.jpg

09_29-FruitFlyEyes_UP.jpg

09_29aFruitFlyEyes_UP.jpg

09_29bFruitFlyEyes_UP.jpg

09_30-SexLinkedInherit_L.jpg

09_30-SexLinkedInherit_U.jpg

09_30aSexLinkedInherit_L.jpg

09_30aSexLinkedInherit_U.jpg

09_30bSexLinkedInherit_L.jpg

09_30bSexLinkedInherit_U.jpg

09_30cSexLinkedInherit_L.jpg

09_30cSexLinkedInherit_U.jpg

09_31Colorblindness_U.jpg

09_32HemophiliaPedigree_CL.jpg

09_32HemophiliaPedigree_CNL.jpg

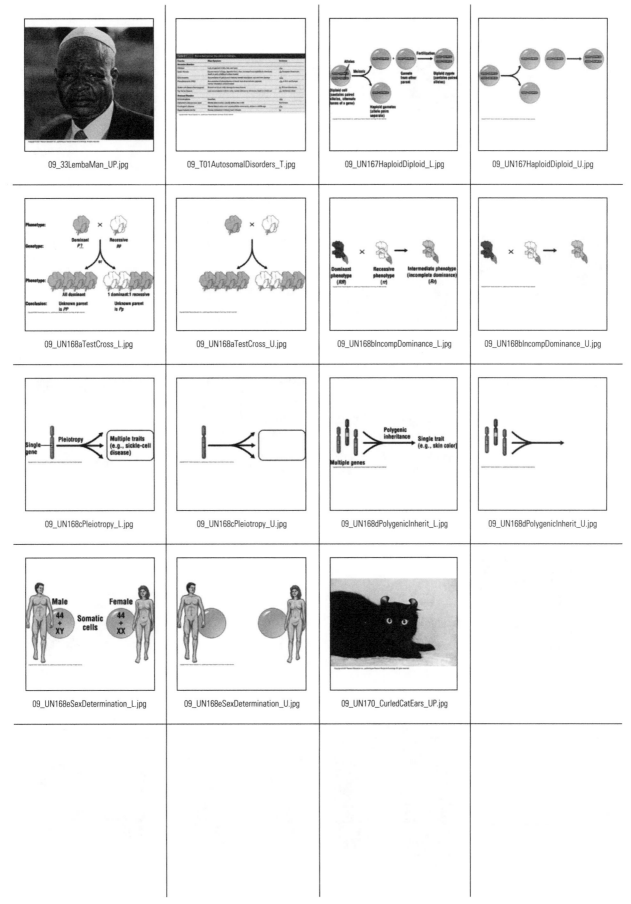

09_33LembaMan_UP.jpg

09_T01AutosomalDisorders_T.jpg

09_UN167HaploidDiploid_L.jpg

09_UN167HaploidDiploid_U.jpg

09_UN168aTestCross_L.jpg

09_UN168aTestCross_U.jpg

09_UN168bIncompDominance_L.jpg

09_UN168bIncompDominance_U.jpg

09_UN168cPleiotropy_L.jpg

09_UN168cPleiotropy_U.jpg

09_UN168dPolygenicInherit_L.jpg

09_UN168dPolygenicInherit_U.jpg

09_UN168eSexDetermination_L.jpg

09_UN168eSexDetermination_U.jpg

09_UN170_CurledCatEars_UP.jpg

Chapter 10 The Structure and Functions of DNA

10_00aHIVpositive_LP.jpg

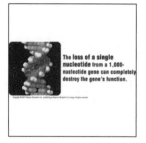

10_00bDNAdoubleHelix_LP.jpg

10_00cVirus_LP.jpg

10_00dTobacoFireflyRecom_LP.jpg

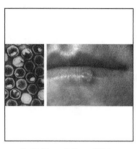

10_00xHerpesCollage_XUP.jpg

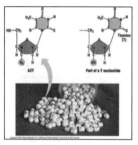

10_01-AZTnucleotide_CL.jpg

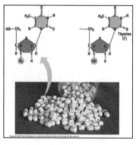

10_01-AZTnucleotide_CNL.jpg

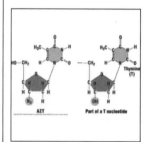

10_01aAZT_L.jpg

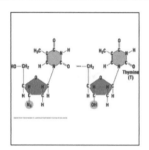

10_01aAZT_U.jpg

10_01bAZTphoto_UP.jpg

10_02aHersheyChaseExp_A.swf

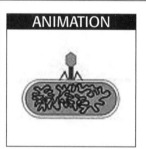

10_02bPhageT2Reproductio_A.swf

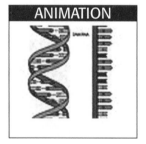

10_02DNAandRNAStructure_A.swf

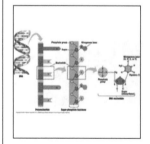

10_02DNAstructur_L.jpg

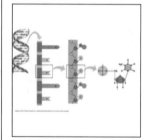

10_02DNAstructur_U.jpg

10_03-DiscovDblHelix_LP.jpg

10_03-DiscovDblHelix_UP.jpg

10_03aWatsonCrick_LP.jpg

10_03aWatsonCrick_UP.jpg

10_03bFranklinAndXray_LP.jpg

10_03bFranklinAndXray_UP.jpg

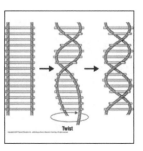

10_04RopeLadderModel_L.jpg

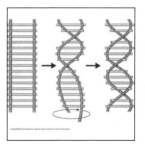

10_04RopeLadderModel_U.jpg

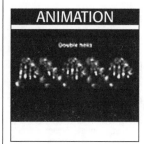

10_05DNADoubleHelix_A.swf

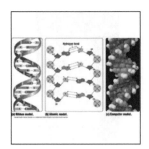

10_05-DNAstructure_L.jpg

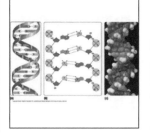

10_05-DNAstructure_U.jpg

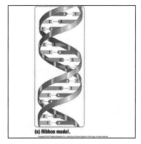

10_05aDNAstructure_L.jpg

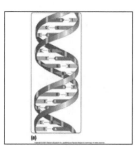

10_05aDNAstructure_U.jpg

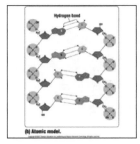

10_05bDNAstructure_L.jpg

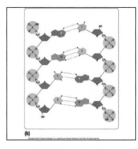

10_05bDNAstructure_U.jpg

10_05cDNAstructure_L.jpg

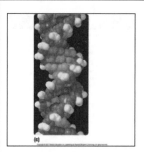

10_05cDNAstructure_U.jpg

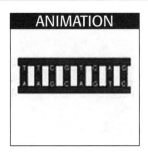

10_06DNAReplicatOverview_A.swf

10_06DNAReplicatReview_A.swf

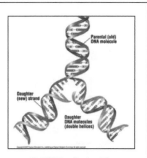

10_06DNAreplication_L.jpg

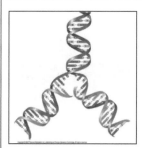

10_06DNAreplication_U.jpg

10_07UVdamage_UP.jpg

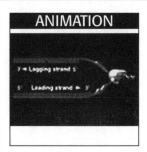

10_08aLaggingStrand_A.swf

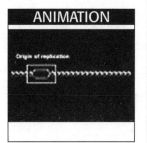

10_08bLeadingStrand_A.swf

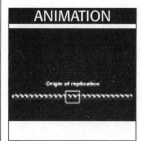

10_08OriginsOfReplicati_A.swf

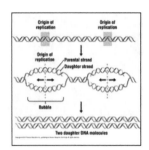

10_08ReplicationBubbles_L.jpg

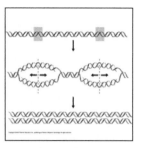

10_08ReplicationBubbles_U.jpg

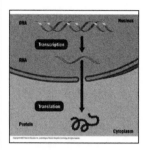

10_09GeneticInfoFlow_L.jpg

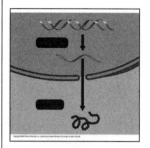

10_09GeneticInfoFlow_U.jpg

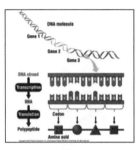

10_10TranscripTranslat_L.jpg

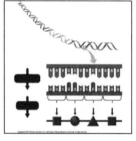

10_10TranscripTranslat_U.jpg

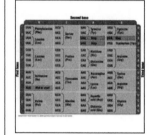

10_11GeneticCode_L.jpg

10_12TobacoFireflyRecom_UP.jpg

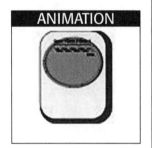

10_13TranscriptionIntro_A.swf

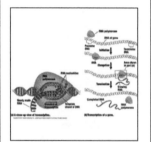

10_13-Transcription_L.jpg

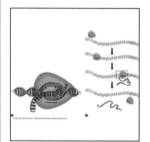

10_13-Transcription_U.jpg

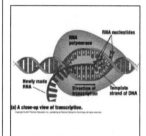

10_13aTranscription_L.jpg

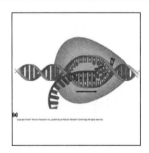

10_13aTranscription_U.jpg

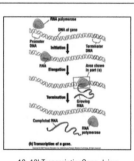

10_13bTranscriptionGene_L.jpg

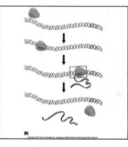

10_13bTranscriptionGene_U.jpg

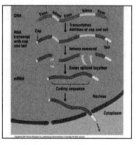

10_14mRNAproduction_L.jpg

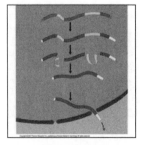

10_14mRNAproduction_U.jpg

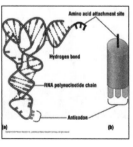

10_15tRNAstructure_L.jpg

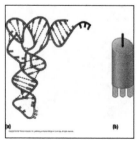

10_15tRNAstructure_U.jpg

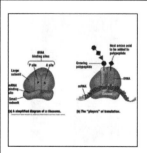

10_16-RibosomeStructure_L.jpg

10_16-RibosomeStructure_U.jpg

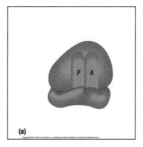

10_16aRibosomeStructure_L.jpg

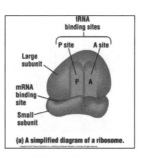

10_16aRibosomeStructure_U.jpg

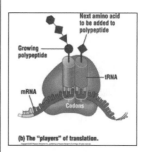

10_16bRibosomeStructure_L.jpg

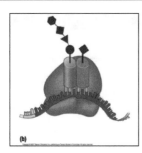

10_16bRibosomeStructure_U.jpg

10_17mRNA_L.jpg

10_17mRNA_U.jpg

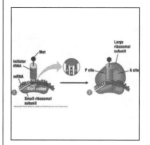

10_18Initiation_L.jpg

10_18Initiation_U.jpg

10_19TranslationIntro_A.swf

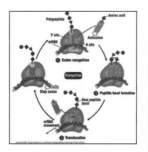

10_19Elongation_L.jpg

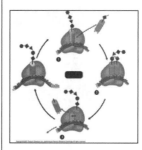

10_19Elongation_U.jpg

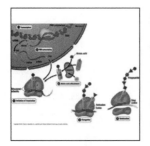

10_20TranscripTranslat_L.jpg

10_20TranscripTranslat_U.jpg

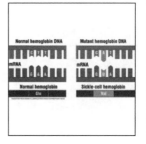

10_21SickleCellMutation_L.jpg

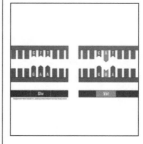

10_21SickleCellMutation_U.jpg

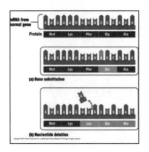

10_22-Mutations_L.jpg

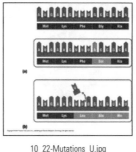

10_22-Mutations_U.jpg

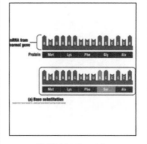

10_22aMutations_L.jpg

10_22aMutations_U.jpg

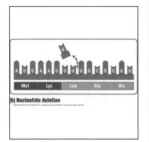

10_22b_Mutations_L.jpg

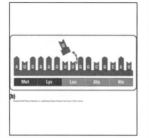

10_22bMutations_U.jpg

10_23MutationDiversity_UP.jpg

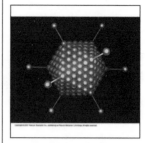

10_24Adenovirus_UP.jpg

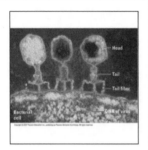

10_25PhageInfectsCell_LP.jpg

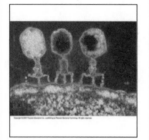

10_25PhageInfectsCell_UP.jpg

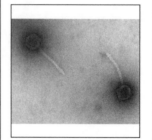

10_25xPhages_XUP.jpg

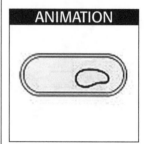

10_26LysogenicLyticCycles_A.swf

10_26PhageT4LyticCycle_A.swf

10_26PhageReproCyc_1_L.jpg

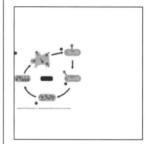

10_26PhageReproCyc_1_U.jpg

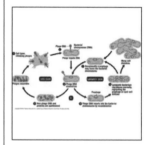

10_26PhageReproCyc_2_L.jpg

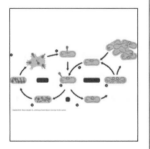

10_26PhageReproCyc_2_U.jpg

10_27TobaccoMosaicVirus_CL.jpg

10_27TobaccoMosaicVirus_CNL.jpg

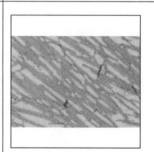

10_27xTobaccoVirusPhoto_XUP.jpg

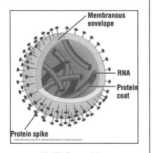

10_28Influenza_L.jpg

10_28Influenza_U.jpg

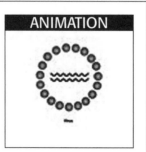

10_29EnvelopedVirus_L.jpg

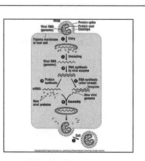

10_29SimpViralReproCycle_A.swf

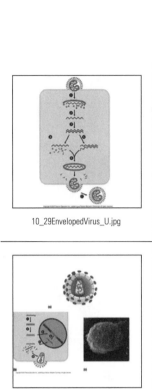

10_29EnvelopedVirus_U.jpg

10_29xPolioVictim_XUP.jpg

10_30HIVReproCycle_A.swf

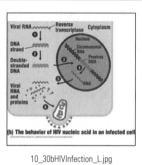

10_30-HIV_CL.jpg

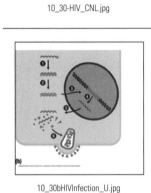

10_30-HIV_CNL.jpg

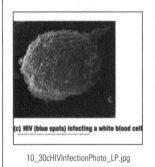

10_30aHIV_L.jpg

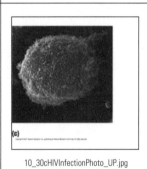

10_30aHIV_U.jpg

10_30bHIVInfection_L.jpg

10_30bHIVInfection_U.jpg

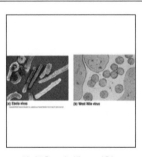

10_30cHIVInfectionPhoto_LP.jpg

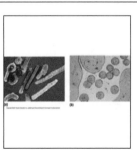

10_30cHIVInfectionPhoto_UP.jpg

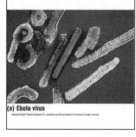

10_30x1HIVinfectionTEM_XUP.jpg

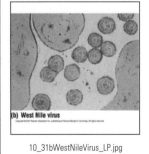

10_30x2AIDSquilt_XUP.jpg

10_31-EmergingViruses_LP.jpg

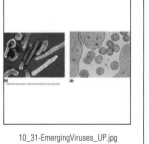

10_31-EmergingViruses_UP.jpg

10_31aEbolaVirus_LP.jpg

10_31aEbolaVirus_UP.jpg

10_31bWestNileVirus_LP.jpg

10_31bWestNileVirus_UP.jpg

10_31xDeerMouse_XUP.jpg

10_32SARSvirus_UP.jpg

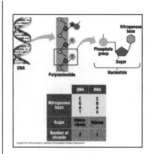

10_33AvianFlu_UP.jpg

10_UN196aDNAstructure_L.jpg

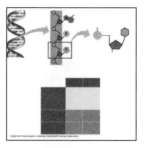

10_UN196aDNAstructure_U.jpg

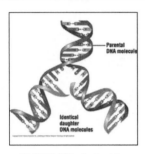

10_UN196bDNAreplication_L.jpg

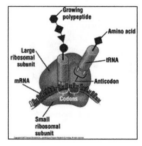

10_UN196bDNAreplication_U.jpg

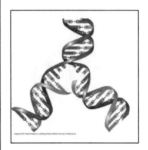

10_UN197Translation_L.jpg

10_UN197Translation_U.jpg

Chapter 11 How Genes are Controlled

11_00aSheepClone_LP.jpg

11_00bIceCream_LP.jpg

11_00cChicken_LP.jpg

11_00dSmokingCancer_LP.jpg

11_01-Clones_UP.jpg

11_01aClones_LP.jpg

11_01aClones_UP.jpg

11_01bClones_LP.jpg

11_01bClones_UP.jpg

11_01cClones_LP.jpg

11_01cClones_UP.jpg

11_02-HumanCells_LP.jpg

11_02-HumanCells_UP.jpg

11_02aHumanCells_LP.jpg

11_02aHumanCells_UP.jpg

11_02bHumanCells_LP.jpg

11_02bHumanCells_UP.jpg

11_02cHumanCells_LP.jpg

11_02cHumanCells_UP.jpg

11_02dHumanCells_LP.jpg

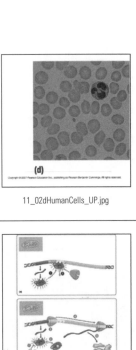

11_02dHumanCells_UP.jpg

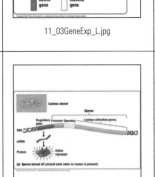

11_03GeneExp_L.jpg

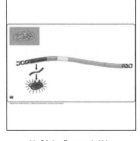

11_03GeneExp_U.jpg

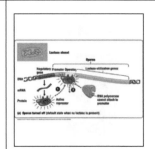

11_04-LacOperon_L.jpg

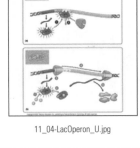

11_04-LacOperon_U.jpg

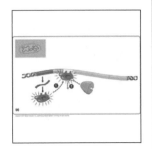

11_04aLacOperon_1_L.jpg

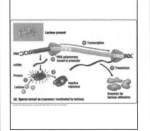

11_04aLacOperon_1_U.jpg

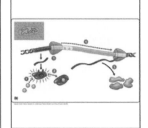

11_04aLacOperon_2_L.jpg

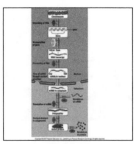

11_04aLacOperon_2_U.jpg

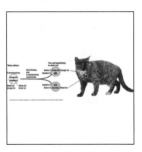

11_04bLacOperon_L.jpg

11_04bLacOperon_U.jpg

11_05RegGeneExp_L.jpg

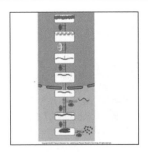

11_05RegGeneExp_U.jpg

11_06-XchromCats_CL.jpg

11_06-XchromCats_CNL.jpg

11_06xCalicoCat_XUP.jpg

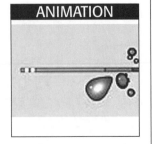

ANIMATION

11_07TranscripInitiation_A.swf

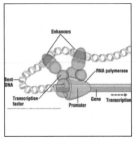

11_07EukGeneReg_L.jpg

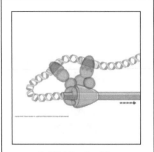

11_07EukGeneReg_U.jpg

ANIMATION

11_08BlockingTranslatio_A.swf

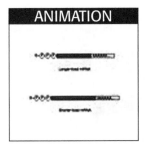

11_08mRNADegradation_A.swf

11_08ProteinProcessing_A.swf

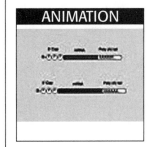

11_08RNAProcessing_A.swf

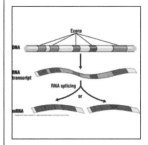

11_08SpliceRNA_L.jpg

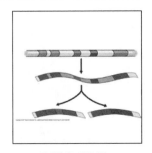

11_08SpliceRNA_U.jpg

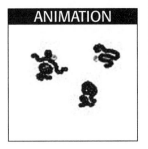

11_09ProteinDegradation_A.swf

11_09InsulinMolecule_L.jpg

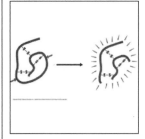

11_09InsulinMolecule_U.jpg

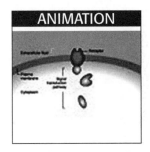

11_10aSignalingOverview_A.swf

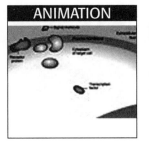

11_10bCellSignaling_A.swf

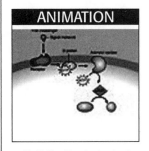

11_10cSignalTransduction_A.swf

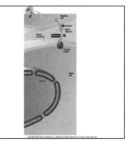

11_10CellSignal_1_L.jpg

11_10CellSignal_1_U.jpg

11_10CellSignal_2_L.jpg

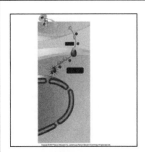

11_10CellSignal_2_U.jpg

11_10CellSignal_3_L.jpg

11_10CellSignal_3_U.jpg

11_10CellSignal_4_L.jpg

11_10CellSignal_4_U.jpg

11_11DNAmicroarray_1_L.jpg

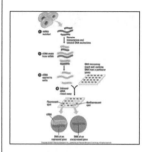

11_11DNAmicroarray_1_U.jpg

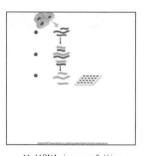

11_11DNAmicroarray_2_L.jpg

11_11DNAmicroarray_2_U.jpg

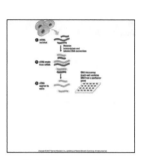

11_11DNAmicroarray_3_L.jpg

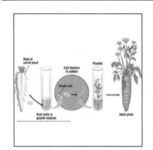

11_11DNAmicroarray_3_U.jpg

11_11DNAmicroarray_CL.jpg

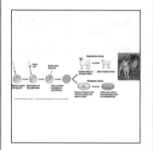

11_11DNAmicroarray_CNL.jpg

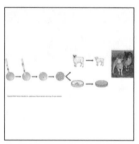

11_11xDNAMicroarray_XUP.jpg

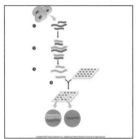

11_12CarrotClone_L.jpg

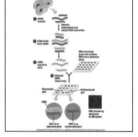

11_12CarrotClone_U.jpg

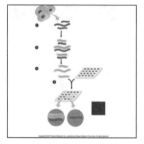

11_13MammalClone_CL.jpg

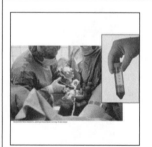

11_13MammalClone_CNL.jpg

11_14GMpiglets_UP.jpg

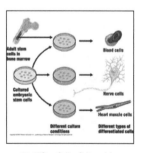

11_15StemCellswCulture_L.jpg

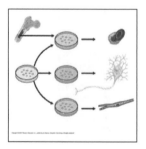

11_15StemCellswCulture_U.jpg

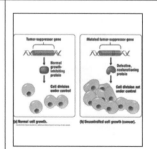

11_16CordBloodBanking_UP.jpg

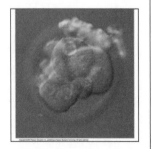

11_17CloneHumanEmbryo_UP.jpg

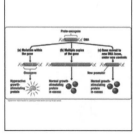

11_18Oncogenes_L.jpg

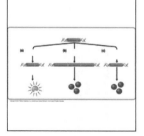

11_18Oncogenes_U.jpg

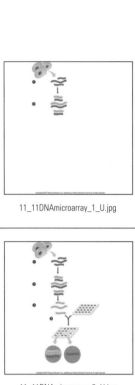

11_19-TumorSupGene_L.jpg

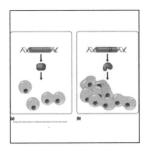

11_19-TumorSupGene_U.jpg

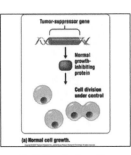

11_19aTumorSupGene_L.jpg

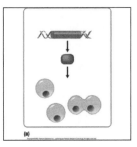

11_19aTumorSupGene_U.jpg

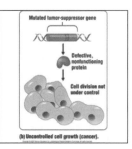

11_19bTumorSupGene_L.jpg

11_19bTumorSupGene_U.jpg

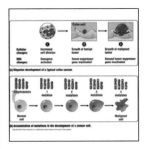

11_20-ColonCanc_L.jpg

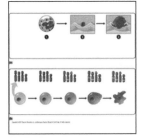

11_20-ColonCanc_U.jpg

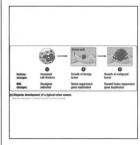

11_20aColonCanc_L.jpg

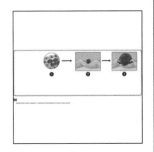

11_20aColonCanc_U.jpg

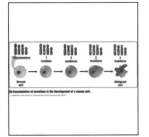

11_20bCancDevel_L.jpg

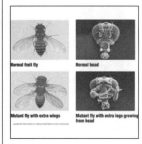

11_20bCancDevel_U.jpg

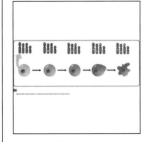

11_21FruitFlies_LP.jpg

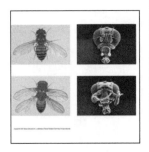

11_21FruitFlies_UP.jpg

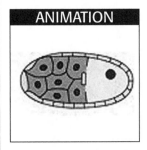

11_22HeadTailAxisFruitFl_A.swf

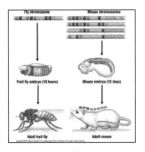

11_22HomeotGenes_L.jpg

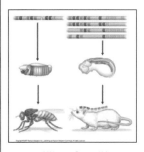

11_22HomeotGenes_U.jpg

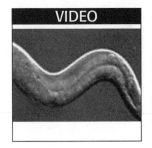

11_22CElegansCrawl_SV.mpg

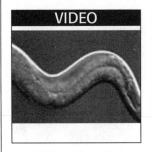

11_22CElegansCrawl_VT.swf

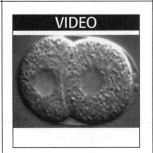

11_22CElegansEmbryo_SV.mpg

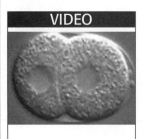

11_22CElegansEmbryo_VT.swf

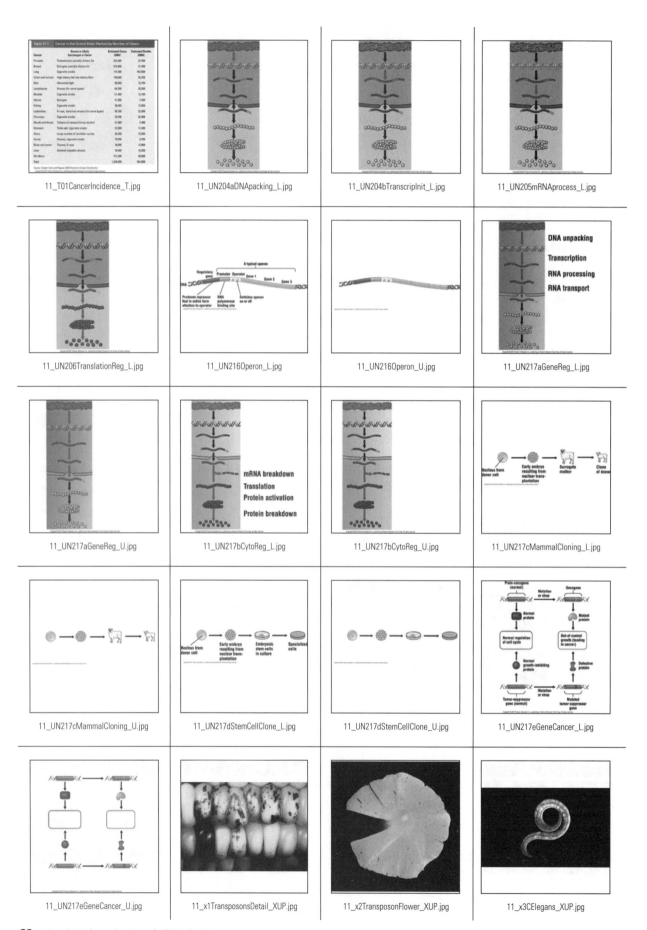

11_T01CancerIncidence_T.jpg

11_UN204aDNApacking_L.jpg

11_UN204bTranscripInit_L.jpg

11_UN205mRNAprocess_L.jpg

11_UN206TranslationReg_L.jpg

11_UN216Operon_L.jpg

11_UN216Operon_U.jpg

11_UN217aGeneReg_L.jpg

11_UN217aGeneReg_U.jpg

11_UN217bCytoReg_L.jpg

11_UN217bCytoReg_U.jpg

11_UN217cMammalCloning_L.jpg

11_UN217cMammalCloning_U.jpg

11_UN217dStemCellClone_L.jpg

11_UN217dStemCellClone_U.jpg

11_UN217eGeneCancer_L.jpg

11_UN217eGeneCancer_U.jpg

11_x1TransposonsDetail_XUP.jpg

11_x2TransposonFlower_XUP.jpg

11_x3CElegans_XUP.jpg

11_x4Drosophila_XUP.jpg

Chapter 12 DNA Technology

12_00aDNAprints_LP.jpg

12_00bTomatoes_LP.jpg

12_00cHumans_LP.jpg

12_00dEColi_LP.jpg

12_01RewardPoster_UP.jpg

12_02DNAtech_L.jpg

12_02DNAtech_U.jpg

12_03InsulinProduction_UP.jpg

12_03x1HepatiVirus_XUP.jpg

12_03x2ChildSmlpox_XUP.jpg

12_03BiotechLab_SV.mpg

12_03BiotechLab_VT.swf

12_04CornPlants_UP.jpg

12_05GMrice_UP.jpg

12_06GMsheep_UP.jpg

12_07Plasmids_LP.jpg

12_07Plasmids_UP.jpg

12_08CloningAGene_A.swf

12_08GeneCloning_1_L.jpg

12_08GeneCloning_1_U.jpg

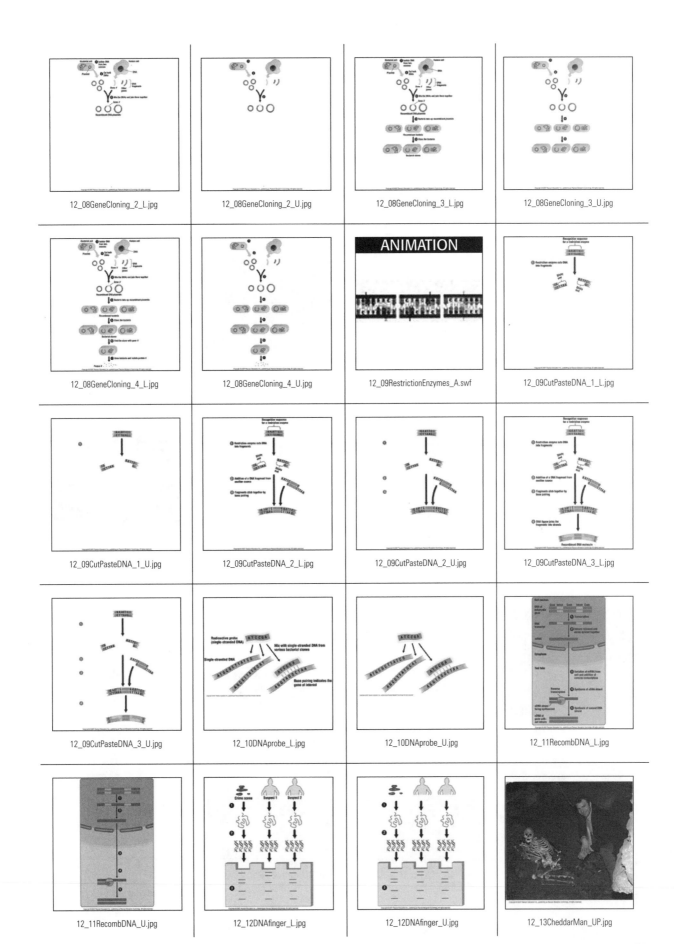

12_08GeneCloning_2_L.jpg

12_08GeneCloning_2_U.jpg

12_08GeneCloning_3_L.jpg

12_08GeneCloning_3_U.jpg

12_08GeneCloning_4_L.jpg

12_08GeneCloning_4_U.jpg

12_09RestrictionEnzymes_A.swf

12_09CutPasteDNA_1_L.jpg

12_09CutPasteDNA_1_U.jpg

12_09CutPasteDNA_2_L.jpg

12_09CutPasteDNA_2_U.jpg

12_09CutPasteDNA_3_L.jpg

12_09CutPasteDNA_3_U.jpg

12_10DNAprobe_L.jpg

12_10DNAprobe_U.jpg

12_11RecombDNA_L.jpg

12_11RecombDNA_U.jpg

12_12DNAfinger_L.jpg

12_12DNAfinger_U.jpg

12_13CheddarMan_UP.jpg

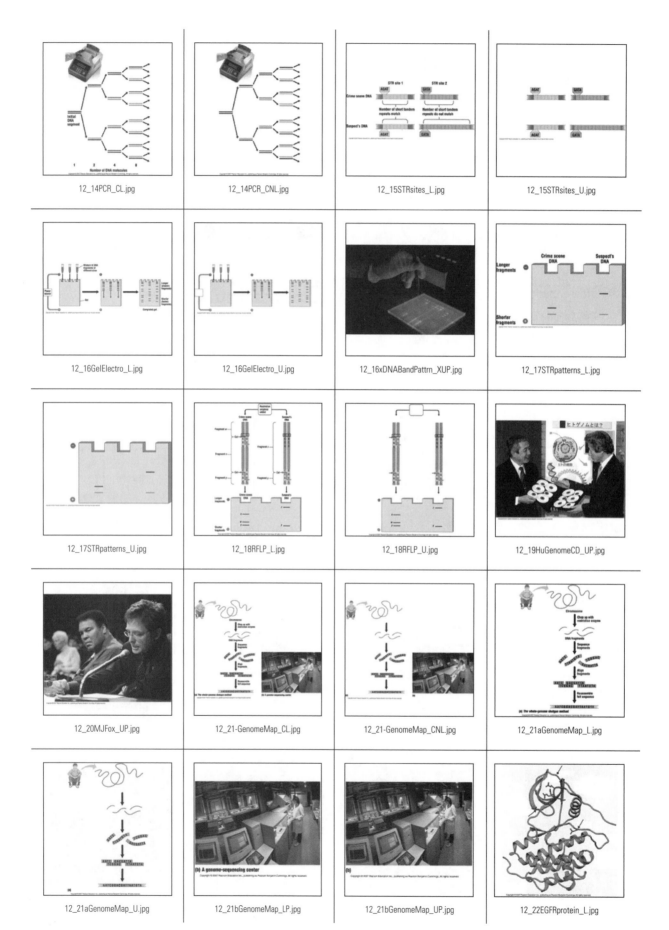

12_14PCR_CL.jpg

12_14PCR_CNL.jpg

12_15STRsites_L.jpg

12_15STRsites_U.jpg

12_16GelElectro_L.jpg

12_16GelElectro_U.jpg

12_16xDNABandPattrn_XUP.jpg

12_17STRpatterns_L.jpg

12_17STRpatterns_U.jpg

12_18RFLP_L.jpg

12_18RFLP_U.jpg

12_19HuGenomeCD_UP.jpg

12_20MJFox_UP.jpg

12_21-GenomeMap_CL.jpg

12_21-GenomeMap_CNL.jpg

12_21aGenomeMap_L.jpg

12_21aGenomeMap_U.jpg

12_21bGenomeMap_LP.jpg

12_21bGenomeMap_UP.jpg

12_22EGFRprotein_L.jpg

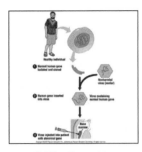

12_23GeneTherapy_L.jpg

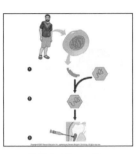

12_23GeneTherapy_U.jpg

12_24MaxSecurityLab_UP.jpg

12_25GMOprotest_UP.jpg

12_26HGHtreatment_UP.jpg

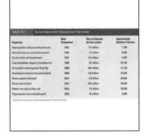

12_T01SequencedGenomes_T.jpg

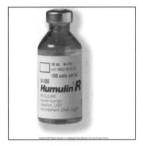

12_UN222Humulin_UP.jpg

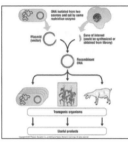

12_UN239aRecombDNA_L.jpg

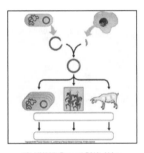

12_UN239aRecombDNA_U.jpg

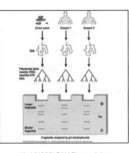

12_UN239bDNAFinger_L.jpg

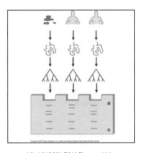

12_UN239bDNAFinger_U.jpg

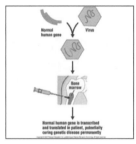

12_UN240HGTherapy_L.jpg

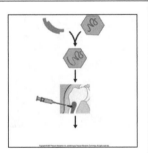

12_UN240HGTherapy_U.jpg

12_x1DNAAnlysCDCLab_XUP.jpg

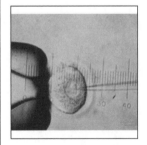

12_x2InjectingDNA_XUP.jpg

13_00aBatWing_LP.jpg

13_00bHumanDiversity_LP.jpg

13_00cPesticide_LP.jpg

13_00dDarwin_LP.jpg

13_01Pesticide_CL.jpg

13_01Pesticide_CNL.jpg

13_02-Camouflage_LP.jpg

13_02-Camouflage_UP.jpg

13_02aCamouflage_LP.jpg

13_02aCamouflage_UP.jpg

13_02bCamouflage_LP.jpg

13_02bCamouflage_UP.jpg

13_02cCamouflage_LP.jpg

13_02cCamouflage_UP.jpg

13_02SeaHorses_SV.mpg

13_02SeaHorses_VT.swf

13_03DarwinTimeline_L.jpg

13_03GrandCanyon_SV.mpg

13_03GrandCanyon_VT.swf

13_03x1Darwin1859_XUP.jpg

13_03x2Darwin1874_XUP.jpg

13_03x3DarwinCartn_XUP.jpg

13_03x4Lamarck_XUP.jpg

13_03x5Lyell_XUP.jpg

13_03x6AlfredWallace_XUP.jpg

13_03x7OrigOfSpecies_XUP.jpg

13_03x8GeorgeCuvr_XUP.jpg

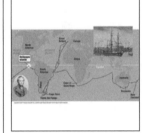

13_04BeagleVoyag_L.jpg

13_04BeagleVoyag_U.jpg

13_05-Iguanas_LP.jpg

13_05-Iguanas_UP.jpg

13_05alguanas_UP.jpg

13_05blguanas_UP.jpg

13_05GalapagosIslands_SV.mpg

13_05GalapagosIslands_VT.swf

13_05MarineIguana_SV.mpg

13_05MarineIguana_VT.swf

13_05SeaLion_SV.mpg

13_05SeaLion_VT.swf

13_05Tortoise_SV.mpg

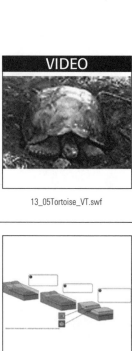

VIDEO

13_05Tortoise_VT.swf

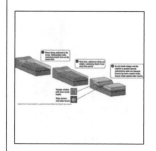

13_06ElephPhylo_L.jpg

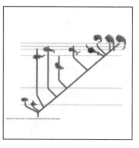

13_06ElephPhylo_U.jpg

13_07FormFossil_L.jpg

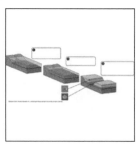

13_07FormFossil_U.jpg

13_08SedStrata_UP.jpg

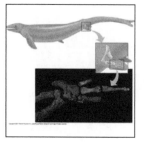

13_09WhaleHindLimb_CL.jpg

13_10Biogeography_LP.jpg

13_10Biogeography_UP.jpg

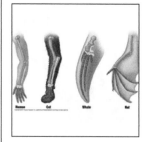

13_11Homology_L.jpg

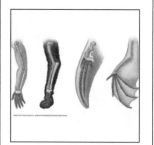

13_11Homology_U.jpg

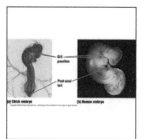

13_12-CompEmbryo_LP.jpg

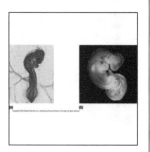

13_12-CompEmbryo_UP.jpg

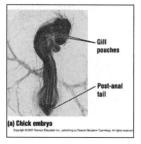

13_12aCompEmbryo_LP.jpg

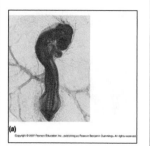

13_12aCompEmbryo_UP.jpg

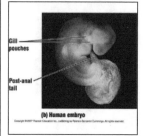

13_12bCompEmbryo_LP.jpg

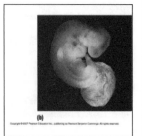

13_12bCompEmbryo_UP.jpg

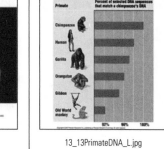

13_13PrimateDNA_L.jpg

13_14-Finches_LP.jpg

13_14-Finches_UP.jpg

(a) The large ground finch.

13_14aFinches_LP.jpg

(a)

13_14aFinches_UP.jpg

(b) The small tree finch.

13_14bFinches_LP.jpg

(b)

13_14bFinches_UP.jpg

(c) The woodpecker finch.

13_14cFinches_LP.jpg

(c)

13_14cFinches_UP.jpg

13_15Overproduction_L.jpg

13_16Variation_L.jpg

13_17-LizHornLength_CL.jpg

13_17aLizHornLength_UP.jpg

13_17bLizHornLength_UP.jpg

13_17cLizHornLength_L.jpg

13_18-Populations_LP.jpg

13_18-Populations_UP.jpg

13_18aPopulations_LP.jpg

13_18aPopulations_UP.jpg

13_18bPopulations_LP.jpg

13_18bPopulations_UP.jpg

ANIMATION

13_19SexualRecombination_A.swf

13_19Polymorphism_UP.jpg

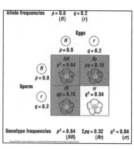

13_20GenePoolDraw_L.jpg

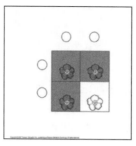

13_20GenePoolDraw_U.jpg

13_21PKUWarning_CL.jpg

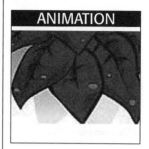

13_22EvolutionaryChanges_A.swf

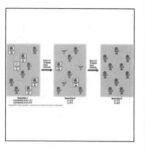

13_22GeneDrift_L.jpg

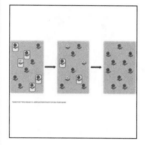

13_22GeneDrift_U.jpg

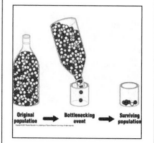

13_23Bottleneck_L.jpg

13_23Bottleneck_U.jpg

13_24BottleneckEffect_UP.jpg

13_25FounderEffect_UP.jpg

13_26HumanDiversity_UP.jpg

13_27Hummingbird_UP.jpg

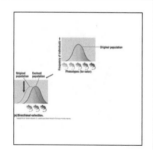

13_28NatSelec_1_L.jpg

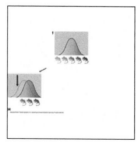

13_28NatSelec_1_U.jpg

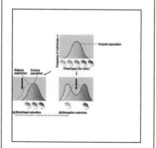

13_28NatSelec_2_L.jpg

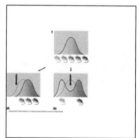

13_28NatSelec_2_U.jpg

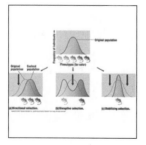

13_28NatSelec_3_L.jpg

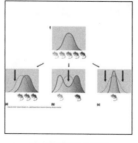

13_28NatSelec_3_U.jpg

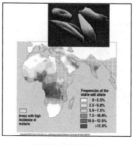

13_29SickleCell_CL.jpg

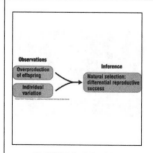

13_UN267aNatSelec_L.jpg

13_UN267aNatSelec_U.jpg

13_UN267bSelection_L.jpg

13_UN267bSelection_U.jpg

Chapter 14 How Biological Diversity Evolves

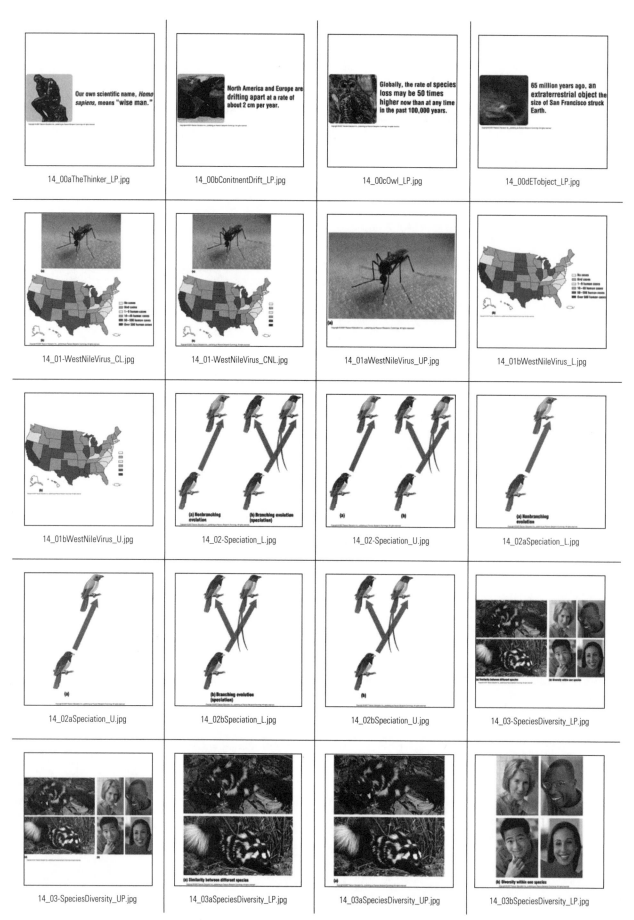

14_00aTheThinker_LP.jpg

14_00bConitnentDrift_LP.jpg

14_00cOwl_LP.jpg

14_00dETobject_LP.jpg

14_01-WestNileVirus_CL.jpg

14_01-WestNileVirus_CNL.jpg

14_01aWestNileVirus_UP.jpg

14_01bWestNileVirus_L.jpg

14_01bWestNileVirus_U.jpg

14_02-Speciation_L.jpg

14_02-Speciation_U.jpg

14_02aSpeciation_L.jpg

14_02aSpeciation_U.jpg

14_02bSpeciation_L.jpg

14_02bSpeciation_U.jpg

14_03-SpeciesDiversity_LP.jpg

14_03-SpeciesDiversity_UP.jpg

14_03aSpeciesDiversity_LP.jpg

14_03aSpeciesDiversity_UP.jpg

14_03bSpeciesDiversity_LP.jpg

14_03bSpeciesDiversity_UP.jpg

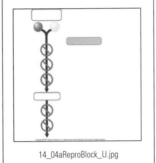

14_03GrandCanyon_SV.mpg

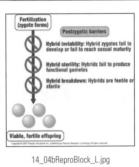

14_03GrandCanyon_VT.swf

14_04-ReproBlock_L.jpg

14_04-ReproBlock_U.jpg

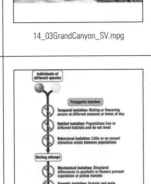

14_04aReproBlock_L.jpg

14_04aReproBlock_U.jpg

14_04bReproBlock_L.jpg

14_04bReproBlock_U.jpg

14_05BoobyCourtship_UP.jpg

14_05AlbatrossCourtshi_SV.mpg

14_05AlbatrossCourtshi_VT.swf

14_05BoobiesCourtship_SV.mpg

14_05BoobiesCourtship_VT.swf

14_05GiraffeCourtship_SV.mpg

14_05GiraffeCourtship_VT.swf

14_06HybridSterility_LP.jpg

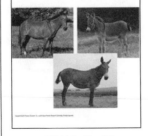

14_06HybridSterility_UP.jpg

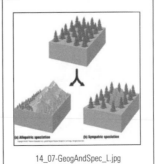

14_07-GeogAndSpec_L.jpg

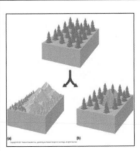

14_07-GeogAndSpec_U.jpg

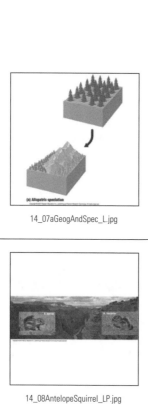

14_07aGeogAndSpec_L.jpg

14_07aGeogAndSpec_U.jpg

14_07bGeogAndSpec_L.jpg

14_07bGeogAndSpec_U.jpg

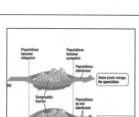

14_08AntelopeSquirrel_LP.jpg

14_08AntelopeSquirrel_UP.jpg

14_08GalapagosIslands_SV.mpg

14_08GalapagosIslands_VT.swf

14_09-AllopatSpec_L.jpg

14_09-AllopatSpec_U.jpg

14_09aAllopatSpec_L.jpg

14_09aAllopatSpec_U.jpg

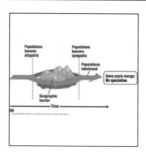

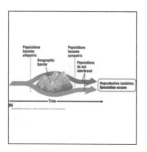

14_09bAllopatSpec_L.jpg

14_09bAllopatSpec_U.jpg

14_10HugodeVries_LP.jpg

14_10HugodeVries_UP.jpg

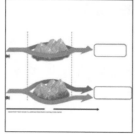

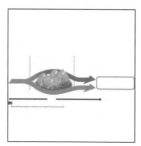

14_11WheatEvolution_L.jpg

14_11WheatEvolution_U.jpg

14_12-TempoOfEvol_L.jpg

14_12-TempoOfEvol_U.jpg

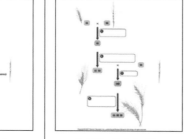

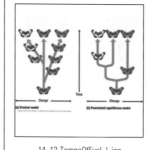

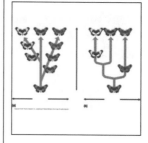

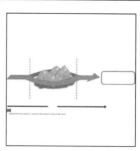

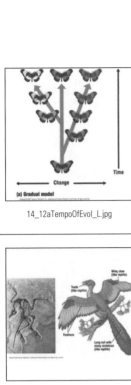

14_12aTempoOfEvol_L.jpg

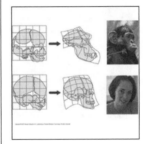

14_12aTempoOfEvol_U.jpg

14_12bTempoOfEvol_L.jpg

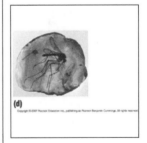

14_12bTempoOfEvol_U.jpg

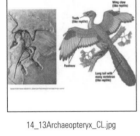

14_13Archaeopteryx_CL.jpg

14_13Archaeopteryx_CNL.jpg

14_14Paedomorphosis_LP.jpg

14_14Paedomorphosis_UP.jpg

14_15AllometricGrowth_A.swf

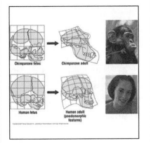

14_15Paedomorph_CL.jpg

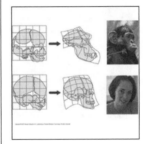

14_15Paedomorph_CNL.jpg

14_16-Fossils_UP.jpg

14_16aFossils_UP.jpg

14_16bFossils_UP.jpg

14_16cFossils_UP.jpg

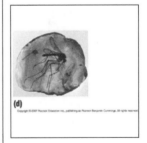

14_16dFossils_UP.jpg

14_16eFossils_UP.jpg

14_16xBurgessShaleColl_XUP.jpg

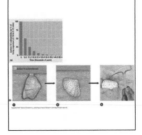

14_17-RadiometricDating_L.jpg

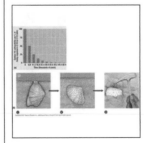

14_17-RadiometricDating_U.jpg

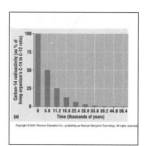

14_17aRadiometricDating_L.jpg

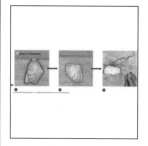

14_17bRadiometricDating_L.jpg

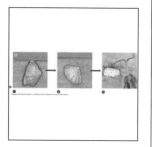

14_17bRadiometricDating_U.jpg

14_18SanAndreasFault_UP.jpg

14_18xSanAndreasFault_XUP.jpg

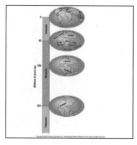

14_19PlateTectonics_L.jpg

14_19PlateTectonics_U.jpg

14_19LavaFlow_SV.swf

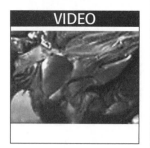

14_19LavaFlow_VT.mpg

14_19VolcanicEruption_SV.mpg

14_19VolcanicEruption_VT.swf

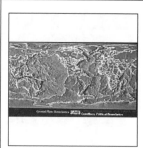

14_19xPlateBoundaries_XUP.jpg

14_20CometImpact_CL.jpg

14_20CometImpact_CNL.jpg

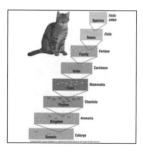

14_21Taxonomy_CL.jpg

14_21Taxonomy_CNL.jpg

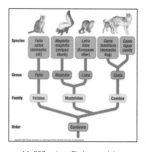

14_22CarnivorePhylogeny_L.jpg

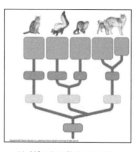

14_22CarnivorePhylogeny_U.jpg

14_23LeafFossil_UP.jpg

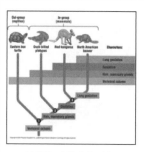

14_24SimpleCladistics_L.jpg

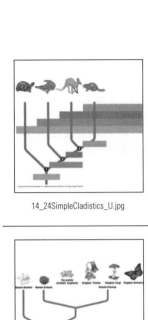

14_24SimpleCladistics_U.jpg

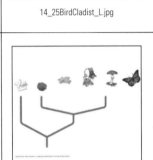

14_25BirdCladist_L.jpg

14_25BirdCladist_U.jpg

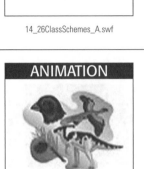

14_26ClassSchemes_A.swf

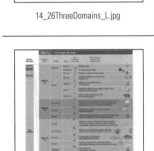

14_26ThreeDomains_L.jpg

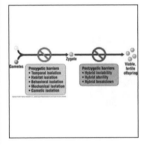

14_26ThreeDomains_U.jpg

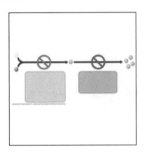

14T_01GeologicRecord_A.swf

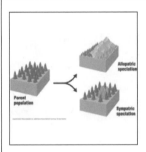

14T_01Macroevolution_A.swf

14_T01GeolTimeScale_T.jpg

14_UN293aBarriers_L.jpg

14_UN293aBarriers_U.jpg

14_UN293bTreeSpec_L.jpg

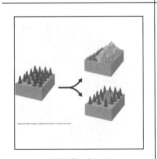

14_UN293bTreeSpec_U.jpg

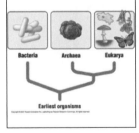

14_UN293c3Domains_L.jpg

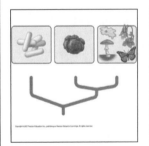

14_UN293c3Domains_U.jpg

Chapter 15 The Evolution of Microbial Life

15_00aSoilBacteria_LP.jpg

15_00bSushi_LP.jpg

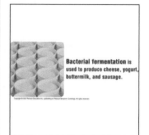

15_00cBacterialFerment_LP.jpg

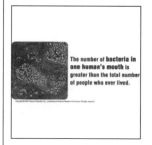

15_00dOralBacteria_LP.jpg

15_01HazardMaterials_UP.jpg

15_02GeologicRecord_A.swf

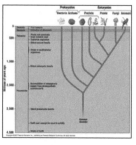

15_02HistoryofLife_L.jpg

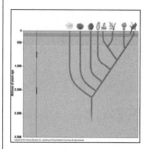

15_02HistoryofLife_U.jpg

15_03AncientEarth_L.jpg

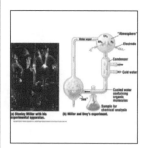

15_04-MillerUreyExperim_CL.jpg

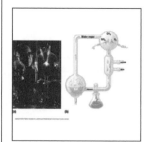

15_04-MillerUreyExperim_CNL.jpg

15_04aMillerUreyExperim_LP.jpg

15_04aMillerUreyExperim_UP.jpg

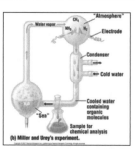

15_04bMillerUreyExperim_L.jpg

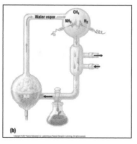

15_04bMillerUreyExperim_U.jpg

15_04x1VolcnLightng_XUP.jpg

15_04x2Lightning_XUP.jpg

15_04x3Pasteur_XUP.jpg

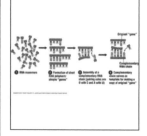

15_05RNAgenes_L.jpg

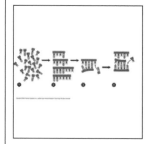

15_05RNAgenes_U.jpg

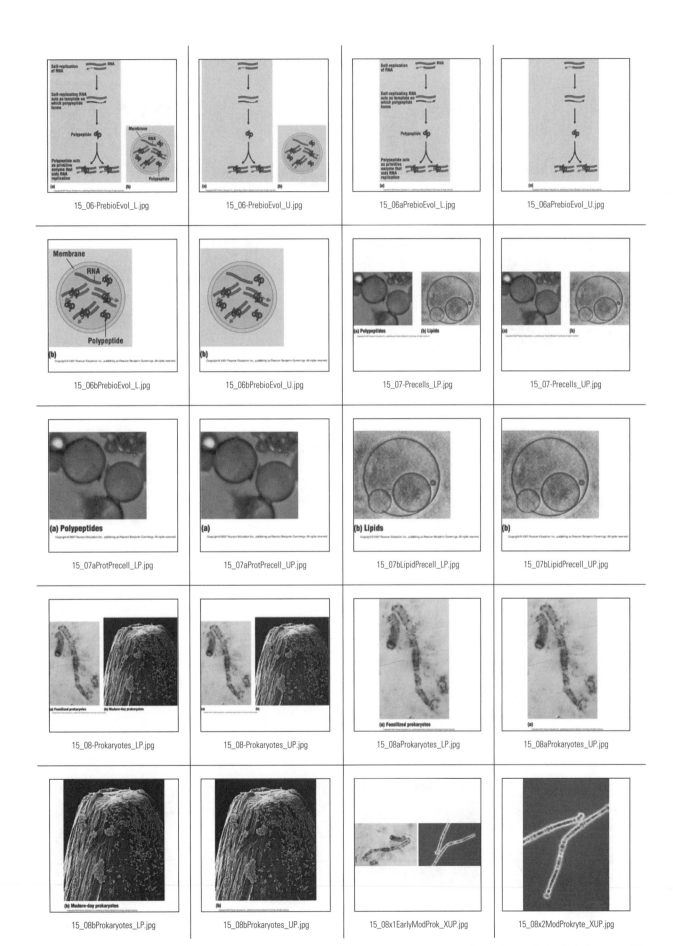

15_06-PrebioEvol_L.jpg

15_06-PrebioEvol_U.jpg

15_06aPrebioEvol_L.jpg

15_06aPrebioEvol_U.jpg

15_06bPrebioEvol_L.jpg

15_06bPrebioEvol_U.jpg

15_07-Precells_LP.jpg

15_07-Precells_UP.jpg

15_07aProtPrecell_LP.jpg

15_07aProtPrecell_UP.jpg

15_07bLipidPrecell_LP.jpg

15_07bLipidPrecell_UP.jpg

15_08-Prokaryotes_LP.jpg

15_08-Prokaryotes_UP.jpg

15_08aProkaryotes_LP.jpg

15_08aProkaryotes_UP.jpg

15_08bProkaryotes_LP.jpg

15_08bProkaryotes_UP.jpg

15_08x1EarlyModProk_XUP.jpg

15_08x2ModProkryte_XUP.jpg

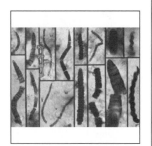

15_08x3FilaProkFosl_XLP.jpg

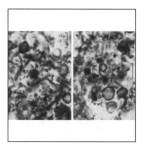

15_08x4UniceProkFosl_XLP.jpg

15_09Halophiles_UP.jpg

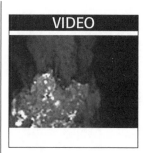

15_09HydrothermalVent_SV.mpg

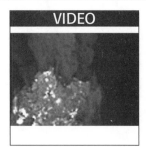

15_09HydrothermalVent_VT.swf

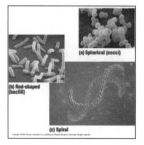

15_10-BacteriaShapes_LP.jpg

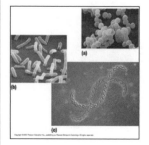

15_10-BacteriaShapes_UP.jpg

15_10aBacteriaShapes_LP.jpg

15_10aBacteriaShapes_UP.jpg

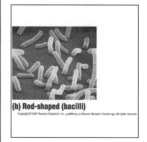

15_10bBacteriaShapes_LP.jpg

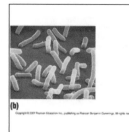

15_10bBacteriaShapes_UP.jpg

15_10cBacteriaShapes_LP.jpg

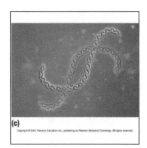

15_10cBacteriaShapes_UP.jpg

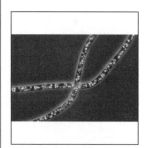

15_10xBeggiaSulfEat_XUP.jpg

15_11-BacterialDiversity_LP.jpg

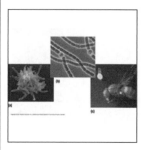

15_11-BacterialDiversity_UP.jpg

15_11aBacterialDiversity_LP.jpg

15_11aBacterialDiversity_UP.jpg

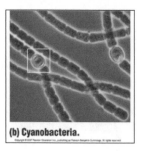

15_11bBacterialDiversity_LP.jpg

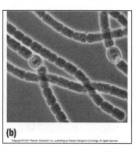

15_11bBacterialDiversity_UP.jpg

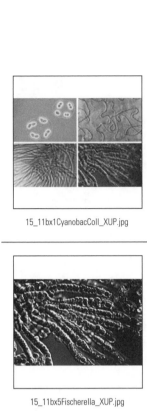

15_11bx1CyanobacColl_XUP.jpg

15_11bx2Gloeothece_XUP.jpg

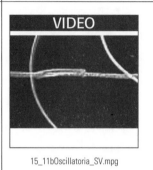

15_11bx3Nostoc_XUP.jpg

15_11bx4Calothrix_XUP.jpg

15_11bx5Fischerella_XUP.jpg

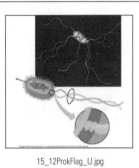

(c) Giant bacterium.

15_11cBacterialDiversity_LP.jpg

(c)

15_11cBacterialDiversity_UP.jpg

VIDEO

15_11bOscillatoria_SV.mpg

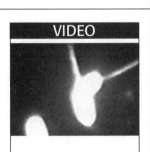

VIDEO

15_11bOscillatoria_VT.swf

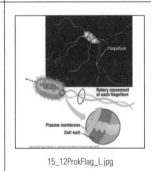

15_12ProkFlag_L.jpg

15_12ProkFlag_U.jpg

VIDEO

15_12SalmonellaFlagell_SV.mpg

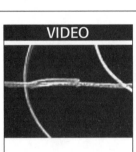

VIDEO

15_12SalmonellaFlagell_VT.swf

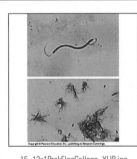 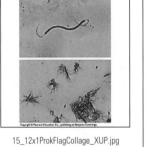

15_12x1ProkFlagCollage_XUP.jpg

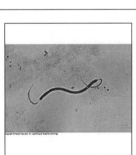

15_12x2TwoProkFlag_XUP.jpg

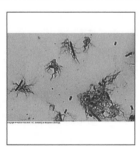

15_12x3ManyProkFlag_XUP.jpg

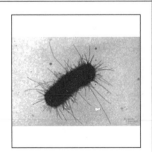

15_12x4Pili_XUP.jpg

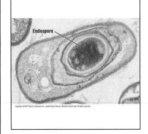

15_13Endospore_LP.jpg

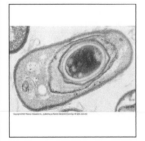

15_13Endospore_UP.jpg

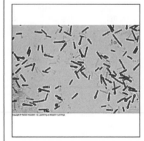

15_13xEndospores_XUP.jpg

15_14HIfluenzae_UP.jpg

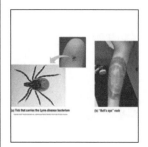

15_15-LymeDisease_LP.jpg

15_15-LymeDisease_UP.jpg

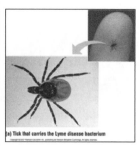

15_15aLymeDisease_LP.jpg

15_15aLymeDisease_UP.jpg

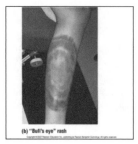

15_15bLymeDisease_LP.jpg

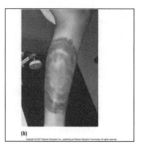

15_15bLymeDisease_UP.jpg

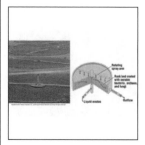

15_16SwgeTreatProcess_CL.jpg

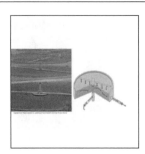

15_16SwgeTreatProcess_CNL.jpg

15_170ilSpillTreat_UP.jpg

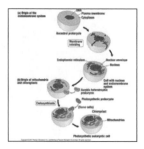

15_18EukEvolution_L.jpg

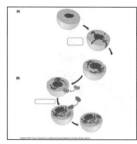

15_18EukEvolution_U.jpg

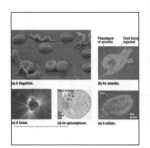

15_19-Protozoans_LP.jpg

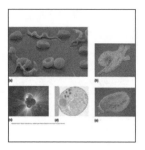

15_19-Protozoans_UP.jpg

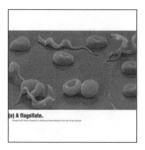

15_19aProtozoans_LP.jpg

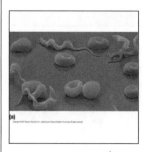

15_19aProtozoans_UP.jpg

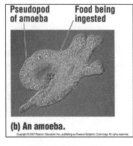

15_19bProtozoans_LP.jpg

15_19bProtozoans_UP.jpg

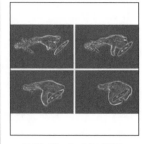

15_19bx1PseudopdiaCol_XUP.jpg

15_19bx2Pseudpda_XUP.jpg

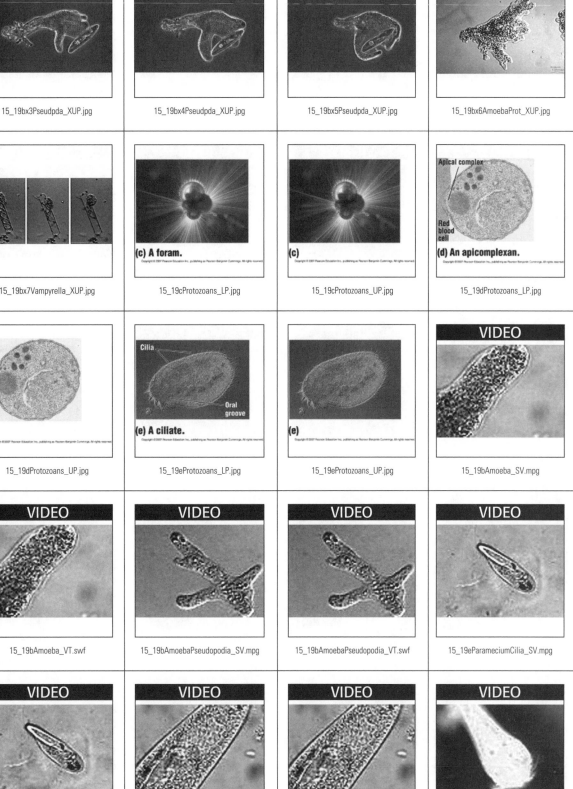

15_19bx3Pseudpda_XUP.jpg

15_19bx4Pseudpda_XUP.jpg

15_19bx5Pseudpda_XUP.jpg

15_19bx6AmoebaProt_XUP.jpg

15_19bx7Vampyrella_XUP.jpg

15_19cProtozoans_LP.jpg

15_19cProtozoans_UP.jpg

15_19dProtozoans_LP.jpg

15_19dProtozoans_UP.jpg

15_19eProtozoans_LP.jpg

15_19eProtozoans_UP.jpg

15_19bAmoeba_SV.mpg

15_19bAmoeba_VT.swf

15_19bAmoebaPseudopodia_SV.mpg

15_19bAmoebaPseudopodia_VT.swf

15_19eParameciumCilia_SV.mpg

15_19eParameciumCilia_VT.swf

15_19eParameciumVacuole_SV.mpg

15_19eParameciumVacuole_VT.swf

15_19eStentor_SV.mpg

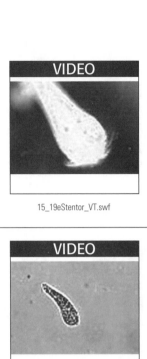

15_19eStentor_VT.swf

15_19eStentorCilia_SV.mpg

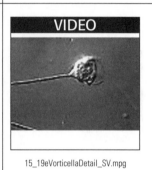

15_19eStentorCilia_VT.swf

15_19EuglenaMotion_SV.mpg

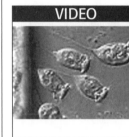

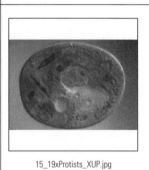

15_19EuglenaMotion_VT.swf

15_19eVorticellaCillia_SV.mpg

15_19eVorticellaCillia_VT.swf

15_19eVorticellaDetail_SV.mpg

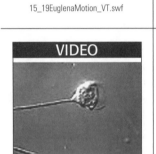

15_19eVorticellaDetail_VT.swf

15_19VorticellaHabitat_SV.mpg

15_19VorticellaHabitat_VT.swf

15_19xProtists_XUP.jpg

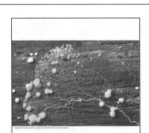

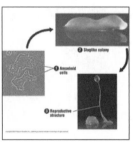

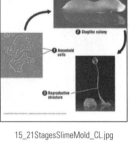

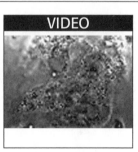

15_20PlasSlimeMold_UP.jpg

15_21StagesSlimeMold_CL.jpg

15_21StagesSlimeMold_CNL.jpg

15_21SlimeMoldStreamin_SV.mpg

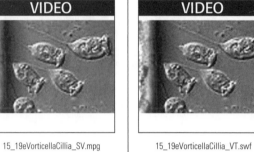

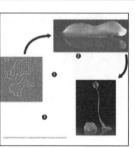

15_21SlimeMoldStreamin_VT.swf

15_21SlimeMoldZoom_SV.mpg

15_21SlimeMoldZoom_VT.swf

15_21x1Dictyostelium_XUP.jpg

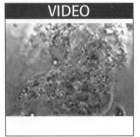

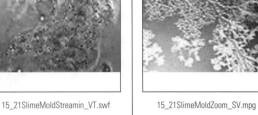

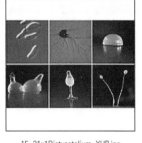

15_21x2SlimeMoldSpor_XUP.jpg

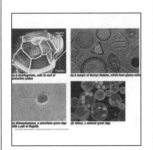

15_22-Algae_LP.jpg

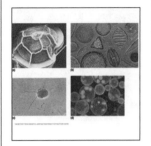

15_22-Algae_UP.jpg

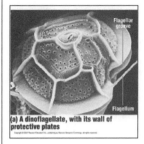

15_22aAlgae_LP.jpg

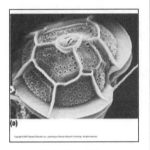

15_22aAlgae_UP.jpg

15_22bAlgae_LP.jpg

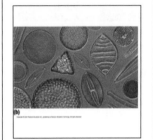

15_22bAlgae_UP.jpg

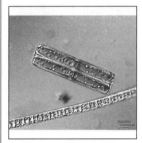

15_22bxPinnulariaDivide_XUP.jpg

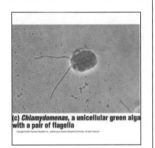

15_22cAlgae_LP.jpg

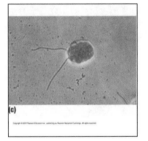

15_22cAlgae_UP.jpg

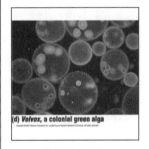

15_22dAlgae_LP.jpg

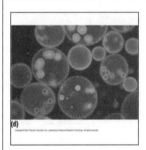

15_22dAlgae_UP.jpg

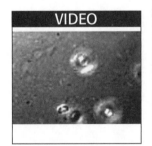

15_22aDinoflagellate_SV.mpg

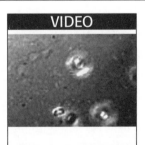

15_22aDinoflagellate_VT.swf

15_22bDiatomsMoving_SV.mpg

15_22bDiatomsMoving_VT.swf

15_22bVariousDiatoms_SV.mpg

15_22bVariousDiatoms_VT.swf

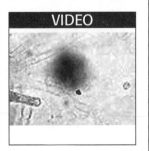

15_22bWaterMoldOogonium_SV.mpg

15_22bWaterMoldOogonium_VT.swf

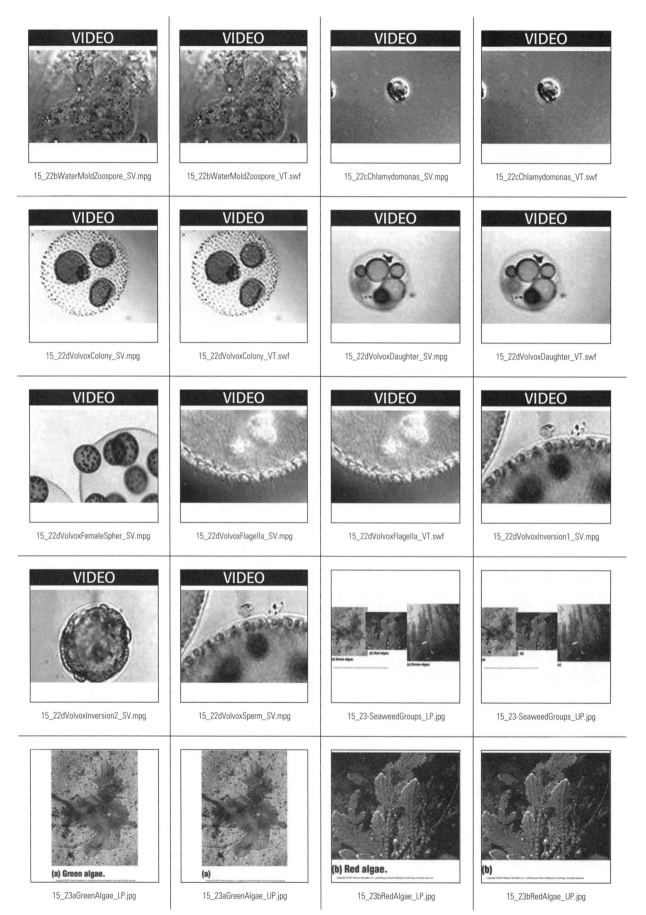

15_22bWaterMoldZoospore_SV.mpg	15_22bWaterMoldZoospore_VT.swf	15_22cChlamydomonas_SV.mpg	15_22cChlamydomonas_VT.swf
15_22dVolvoxColony_SV.mpg	15_22dVolvoxColony_VT.swf	15_22dVolvoxDaughter_SV.mpg	15_22dVolvoxDaughter_VT.swf
15_22dVolvoxFemaleSpher_SV.mpg	15_22dVolvoxFlagella_SV.mpg	15_22dVolvoxFlagella_VT.swf	15_22dVolvoxInversion1_SV.mpg
15_22dVolvoxInversion2_SV.mpg	15_22dVolvoxSperm_SV.mpg	15_23-SeaweedGroups_LP.jpg	15_23-SeaweedGroups_UP.jpg
15_23aGreenAlgae_LP.jpg	15_23aGreenAlgae_UP.jpg	15_23bRedAlgae_LP.jpg	15_23bRedAlgae_UP.jpg

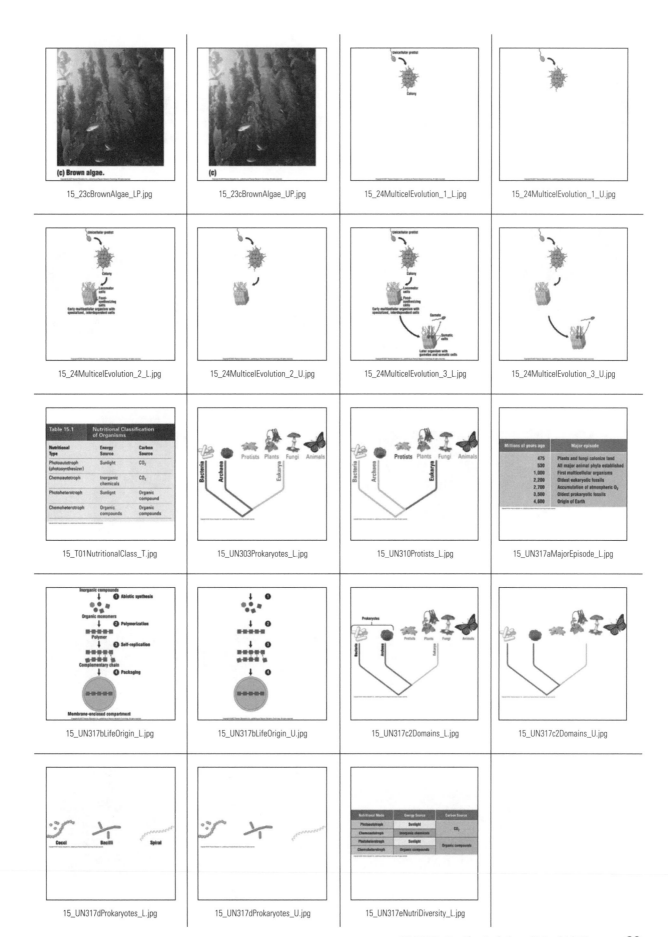

15_23cBrownAlgae_LP.jpg

15_23cBrownAlgae_UP.jpg

15_24MulticelEvolution_1_L.jpg

15_24MulticelEvolution_1_U.jpg

15_24MulticelEvolution_2_L.jpg

15_24MulticelEvolution_2_U.jpg

15_24MulticelEvolution_3_L.jpg

15_24MulticelEvolution_3_U.jpg

15_T01NutritionalClass_T.jpg

15_UN303Prokaryotes_L.jpg

15_UN310Protists_L.jpg

15_UN317aMajorEpisode_L.jpg

15_UN317bLifeOrigin_L.jpg

15_UN317bLifeOrigin_U.jpg

15_UN317c2Domains_L.jpg

15_UN317c2Domains_U.jpg

15_UN317dProkaryotes_L.jpg

15_UN317dProkaryotes_U.jpg

15_UN317eNutriDiversity_L.jpg

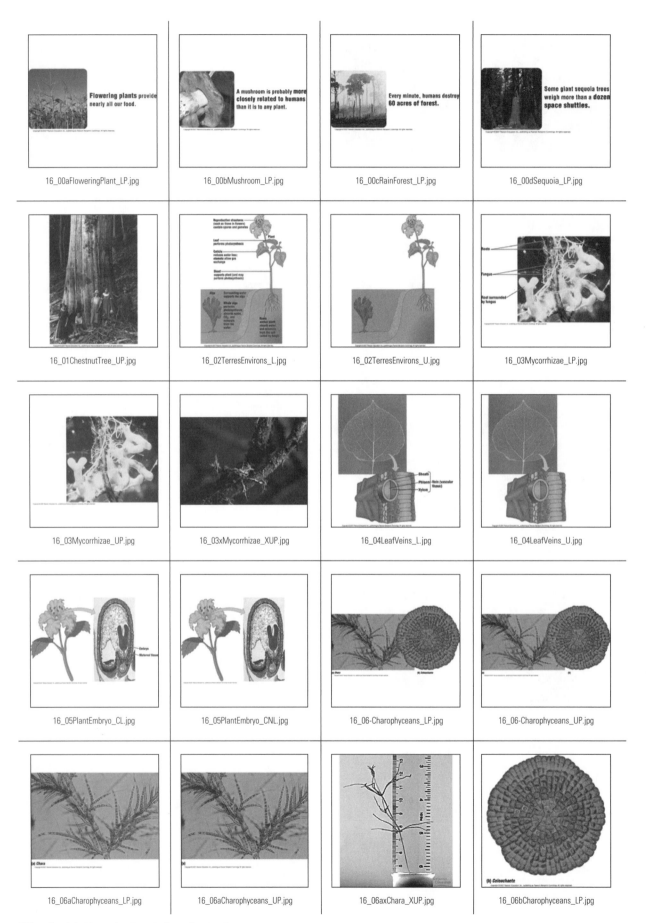

16_00aFloweringPlant_LP.jpg

16_00bMushroom_LP.jpg

16_00cRainForest_LP.jpg

16_00dSequoia_LP.jpg

16_01ChestnutTree_UP.jpg

16_02TerresEnvirons_L.jpg

16_02TerresEnvirons_U.jpg

16_03Mycorrhizae_LP.jpg

16_03Mycorrhizae_UP.jpg

16_03xMycorrhizae_XUP.jpg

16_04LeafVeins_L.jpg

16_04LeafVeins_U.jpg

16_05PlantEmbryo_CL.jpg

16_05PlantEmbryo_CNL.jpg

16_06-Charophyceans_LP.jpg

16_06-Charophyceans_UP.jpg

16_06aCharophyceans_LP.jpg

16_06aCharophyceans_UP.jpg

16_06axChara_XUP.jpg

16_06bCharophyceans_LP.jpg

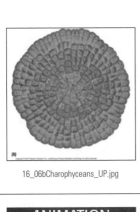

16_06bCharophyceans_UP.jpg

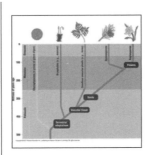

16_07PlantPhylo_L.jpg

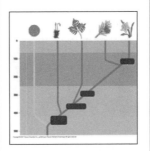

16_07PlantPhylo_U.jpg

16_08PeatMossBog_UP.jpg

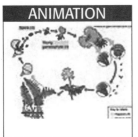

16_09FernLifeCycle_A.swf

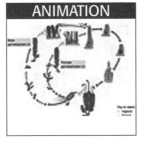

16_09MossLifeCycle_A.swf

16_09PineLifeCycle_A.swf

16_09Moss_LP.jpg

16_09Moss_UP.jpg

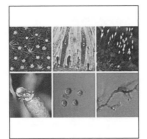

16_09x01MossLifeCycle_XUP.jpg

16_09x02MossGameto_XUP.jpg

16_09x03MossArcheg_XUP.jpg

16_09x04MossSporo_XUP.jpg

16_09x05MossSporang_XUP.jpg

16_09x06MossSpores_XUP.jpg

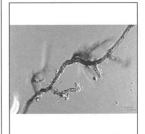

16_09x07MosProtnemta_XUP.jpg

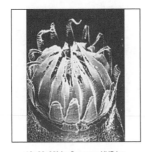

16_09x08MosSporang_XUP.jpg

16_09x09SphagnumMoss_XUP.jpg

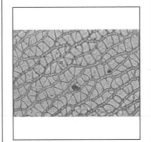

16_09x10SphagnumLeaf_XUP.jpg

16_09x11LeafyLivrwrt_XUP.jpg

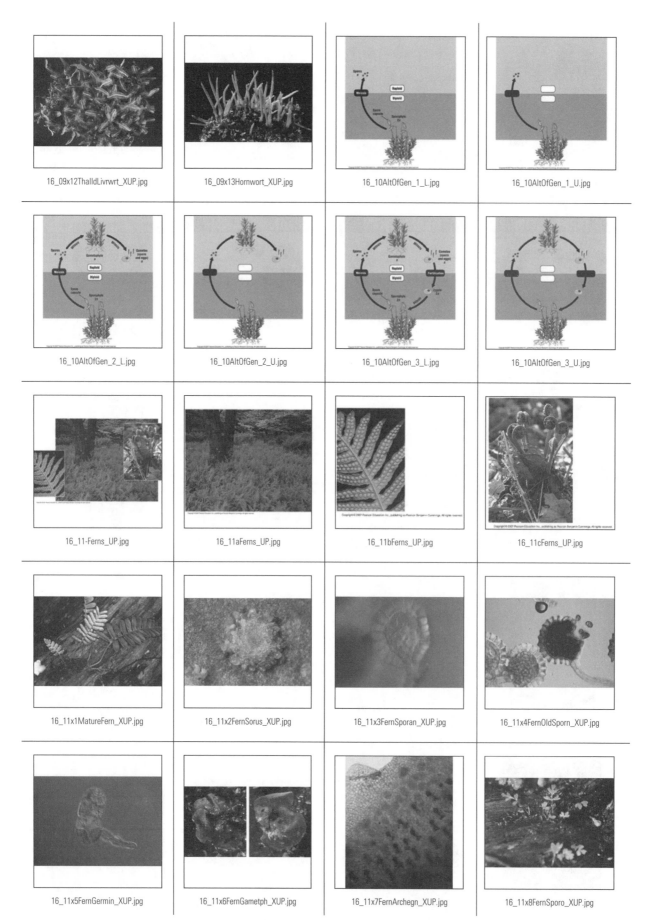

16_09x12ThalldLivrwrt_XUP.jpg

16_09x13Hornwort_XUP.jpg

16_10AltOfGen_1_L.jpg

16_10AltOfGen_1_U.jpg

16_10AltOfGen_2_L.jpg

16_10AltOfGen_2_U.jpg

16_10AltOfGen_3_L.jpg

16_10AltOfGen_3_U.jpg

16_11-Ferns_UP.jpg

16_11aFerns_UP.jpg

16_11bFerns_UP.jpg

16_11cFerns_UP.jpg

16_11x1MatureFern_XUP.jpg

16_11x2FernSorus_XUP.jpg

16_11x3FernSporan_XUP.jpg

16_11x4FernOldSporn_XUP.jpg

16_11x5FernGermin_XUP.jpg

16_11x6FernGametph_XUP.jpg

16_11x7FernArchegn_XUP.jpg

16_11x8FernSporo_XUP.jpg

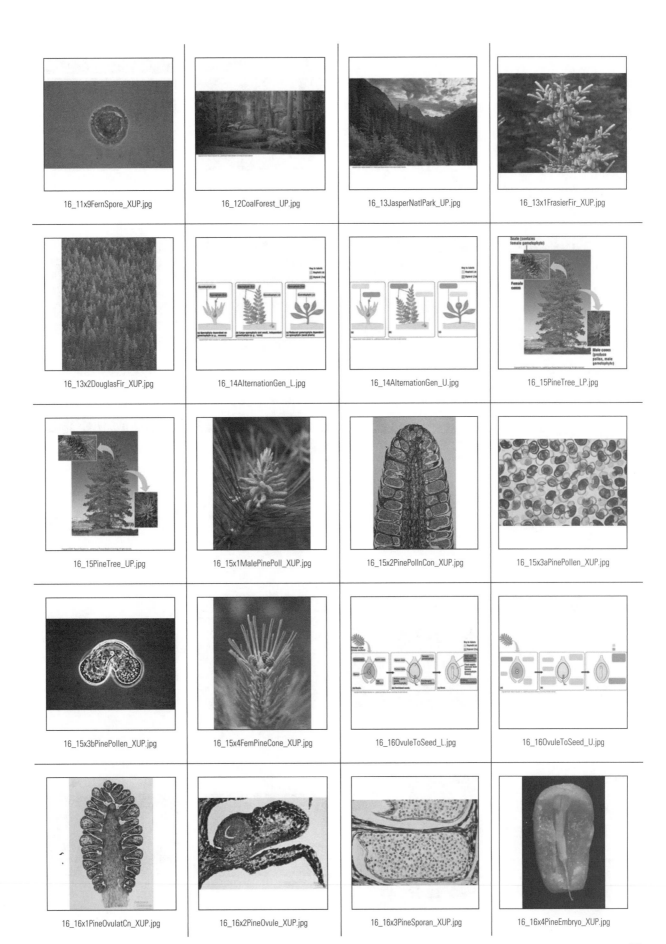

16_11x9FernSpore_XUP.jpg

16_12CoalForest_UP.jpg

16_13JasperNatlPark_UP.jpg

16_13x1FrasierFir_XUP.jpg

16_13x2DouglasFir_XUP.jpg

16_14AlternationGen_L.jpg

16_14AlternationGen_U.jpg

16_15PineTree_LP.jpg

16_15PineTree_UP.jpg

16_15x1MalePinePoll_XUP.jpg

16_15x2PinePollInCon_XUP.jpg

16_15x3aPinePollen_XUP.jpg

16_15x3bPinePollen_XUP.jpg

16_15x4FemPineCone_XUP.jpg

16_16OvuleToSeed_L.jpg

16_16OvuleToSeed_U.jpg

16_16x1PineOvulatCn_XUP.jpg

16_16x2PineOvule_XUP.jpg

16_16x3PineSporan_XUP.jpg

16_16x4PineEmbryo_XUP.jpg

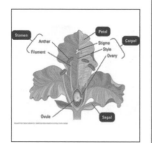

16_17FlowerStructure_L.jpg

16_17FlowerStructure_U.jpg

16_17BatPollinating_SV.mpg

16_17BatPollinating_VT.swf

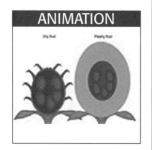

16_17BeePollinating_SV.mpg

16_17BeePollinating_VT.swf

16_17FlowerTimeLapse_SV.mpg

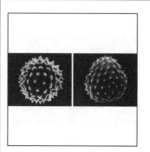

16_17FlowerTimeLapse_VT.swf

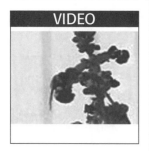

16_18AngioCycle_L.jpg

16_18AngioCycle_U.jpg

16_18aPlantFertilization_A.swf

16_18bSeedDevelopment_A.swf

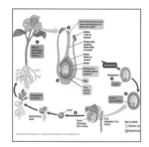

16_18cFruitDevelopment_A.swf

16_18PlantTimeLapse_SV.mpg

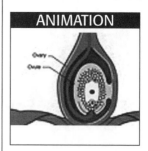

16_18PlantTimeLapse_VT.swf

16_18xPolGrainSEM_XUP.jpg

16_19-FruitsSeeds_LP.jpg

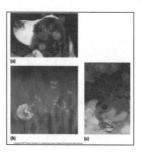

16_19-FruitsSeeds_UP.jpg

16_19aFruitsSeeds_LP.jpg

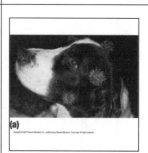

16_19aFruitsSeeds_UP.jpg

(b) Dandelion fruit.

16_19bFruitsSeeds_LP.jpg

(b)

16_19bFruitsSeeds_UP.jpg

(c) Berries.

16_19cFruitsSeeds_LP.jpg

(c)

16_19cFruitsSeeds_UP.jpg

16_19x1PineSdDispl_XUP.jpg

16_19x2DisperColl_XUP.jpg

16_20-Fungi_LP.jpg

16_20-Fungi_UP.jpg

(a) Fly agaric mushrooms.

16_20aFungi_LP.jpg

(a)

16_20aFungi_UP.jpg

(b) A "fairy ring."

16_20bFungi_LP.jpg

(b)

16_20bFungi_UP.jpg

(c) *Pilobolus.*

16_20cFungi_LP.jpg

(c)

16_20cFungi_UP.jpg

16_20cxPilobolus_XUP.jpg

(d) Mold.

16_20dFungi_LP.jpg

(d)

16_20dFungi_UP.jpg

16_20dx1MoldyOrngeCol_XUP.jpg

16_20dx2MoldyOrange_XUP.jpg

16_20dx3Penicillium_XUP.jpg

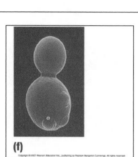

16_20dx4Botrytis_XUP.jpg

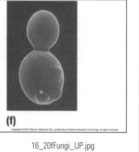

16_20dx5SoilPlate_XUP.jpg

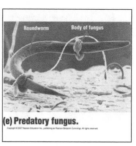

16_20eFungi_LP.jpg

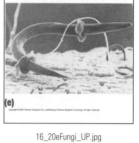

16_20eFungi_UP.jpg

16_20fFungi_LP.jpg

16_20fFungi_UP.jpg

16_20AllomycesZoospore_SV.mpg

16_20AllomycesZoospore_VT.swf

16_20PhlyctochytriumSpor_SV.mpg

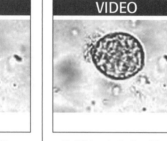

16_20PhlyctochytriumSpor_VT.swf

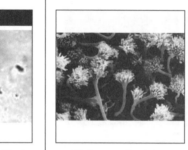

16_20x1Aspergillus_XUP.jpg

16_20x2aGills_XUP.jpg

16_20x2bGillBasidLM_XUP.jpg

16_20x2-GillsBasidCol_XUP.jpg

16_20x3Amanita_XUP.jpg

16_20x4Coprinus_XUP.jpg

16_20x5GrevilBolete_XUP.jpg

16_20x6Morel_XUP.jpg

16_20x7Stinkhorn_XUP.jpg

16_20x8Trametes_XUP.jpg

16_20x9Tremella_XUP.jpg

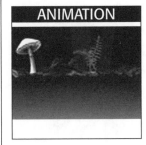

16_21FungalReproNutrition_A.swf

16_21Mycilium_CL.jpg

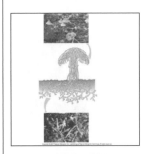

16_21Mycilium_CNL.jpg

16_21x1HyphaeColl_XUP.jpg

16_21x2Septate_XUP.jpg

16_21x3Nonseptate_XUP.jpg

16_22-ParasiticFungi_LP.jpg

16_22-ParasiticFungi_UP.jpg

16_22aParasiticFungi_LP.jpg

16_22aParasiticFungi_UP.jpg

16_22bParasiticFungi_LP.jpg

16_22bParasiticFungi_UP.jpg

16_23-Fungi_LP.jpg

16_23-Fungi_UP.jpg

16_23aTruffles_LP.jpg

16_23aTruffles_UP.jpg

16_23bBlueCheese_LP.jpg

16_23bBlueCheese_UP.jpg

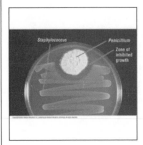

16_24Penicillium_LP.jpg

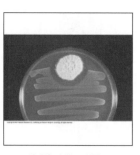
16_24Penicillium_UP.jpg

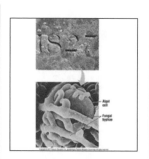
16_25Lichens_LP.jpg

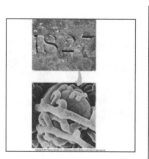
16_25Lichens_UP.jpg

16_25xLichenAnat_XUP.jpg

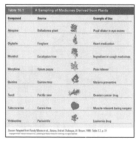
16_T01SamplingMedicines_T.jpg

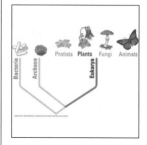
16_UN324Plants_L.jpg

16_UN324Plants_U.jpg

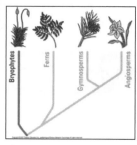
16_UN325Bryophytes_L.jpg

16_UN325Bryophytes_U.jpg

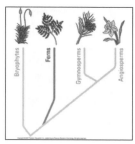
16_UN326Ferns_L.jpg

16_UN326Ferns_U.jpg

16_UN327Gymnosperms_L.jpg

16_UN327Gymnosperms_U.jpg

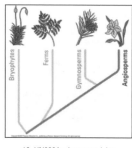
16_UN330Angiosperms_L.jpg

16_UN330Angiosperms_U.jpg

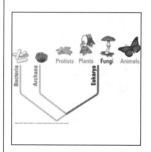
16_UN334Fungi_L.jpg

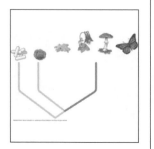
16_UN334Fungi_U.jpg

16_UN340aTerresPlants_L.jpg

16_UN340aTerresPlants_U.jpg

16_UN340bPlantEvol_L.jpg

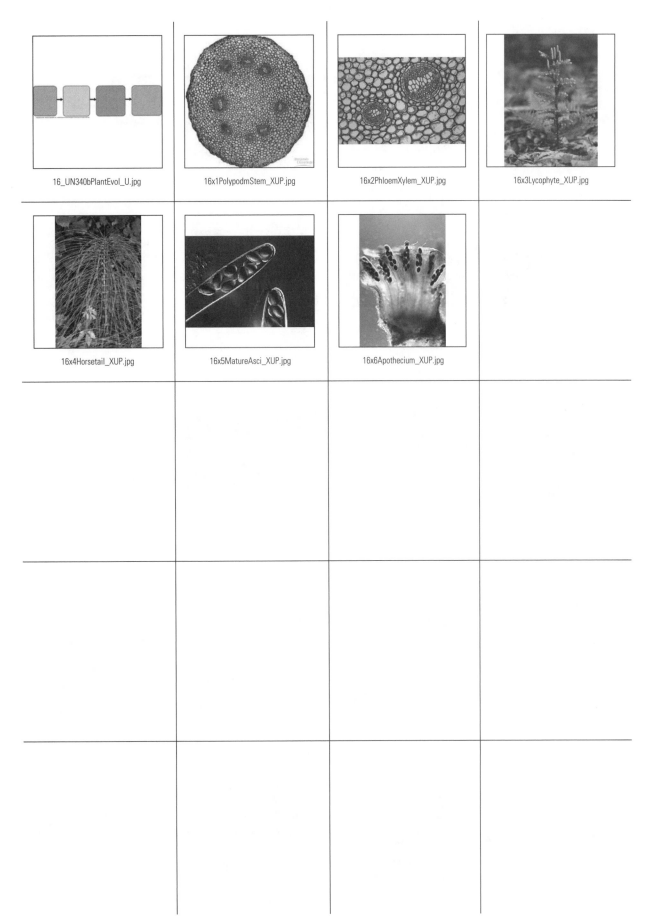

16_UN340bPlantEvol_U.jpg

16x1PolypodmStem_XUP.jpg

16x2PhloemXylem_XUP.jpg

16x3Lycophyte_XUP.jpg

16x4Horsetail_XUP.jpg

16x5MatureAsci_XUP.jpg

16x6Apothecium_XUP.jpg

Chapter 17 The Evolution of Animals

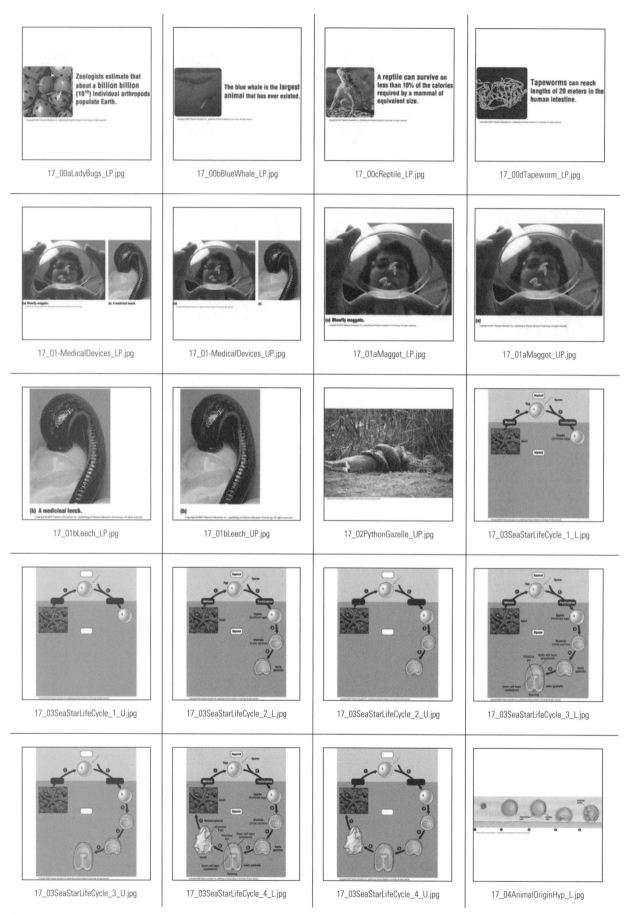

17_00aLadyBugs_LP.jpg

17_00bBlueWhale_LP.jpg

17_00cReptile_LP.jpg

17_00dTapeworm_LP.jpg

17_01-MedicalDevices_LP.jpg

17_01-MedicalDevices_UP.jpg

17_01aMaggot_LP.jpg

17_01aMaggot_UP.jpg

17_01bLeech_LP.jpg

17_01bLeech_UP.jpg

17_02PythonGazelle_UP.jpg

17_03SeaStarLifeCycle_1_L.jpg

17_03SeaStarLifeCycle_1_U.jpg

17_03SeaStarLifeCycle_2_L.jpg

17_03SeaStarLifeCycle_2_U.jpg

17_03SeaStarLifeCycle_3_L.jpg

17_03SeaStarLifeCycle_3_U.jpg

17_03SeaStarLifeCycle_4_L.jpg

17_03SeaStarLifeCycle_4_U.jpg

17_04AnimalOriginHyp_L.jpg

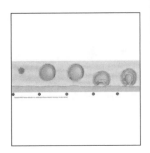

17_04AnimalOriginHyp_U.jpg

17_05-CambrianSea_UP.jpg

17_05aCambrianSea_UP.jpg

17_05bCambrianSea_UP.jpg

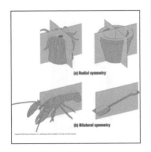

17_05x1BurgessShaleCol_XUP.jpg

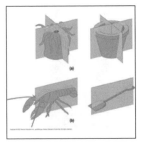

17_05x2CambrianLife_XUP.jpg

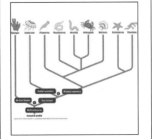

17_06AnimalPhylo_L.jpg

17_06AnimalPhylo_U.jpg

17_07-BodySymmetry_L.jpg

17_07-BodySymmetry_U.jpg

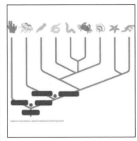

17_07aRadialSymm_L.jpg

17_07aRadialSymm_U.jpg

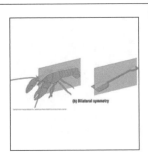

17_07bBilateralSymm_L.jpg

17_07bBilateralSymm_U.jpg

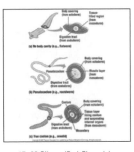

17_08-BilateralBodyPlans_L.jpg

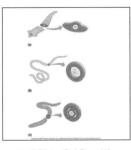

17_08-BilateralBodyPlans_U.jpg

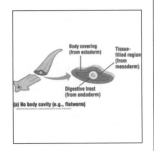

17_08aBilateralBodyPlans_L.jpg

17_08aBilateralBodyPlans_U.jpg

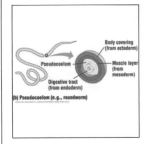

17_08bBilateralBodyPlans_L.jpg

17_08bBilateralBodyPlans_U.jpg

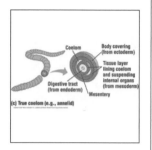

17_08cBilateralBodyPlans_L.jpg

17_08cBilateralBodyPlans_U.jpg

17_09Sponge_UP.jpg

17_09xSponges_XUP.jpg

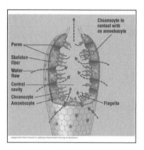

17_10SpongeAnatomy_L.jpg

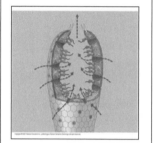

17_10SpongeAnatomy_U.jpg

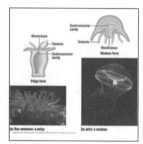

17_11-PolypMedusa_CL.jpg

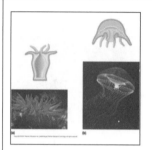

17_11-PolypMedusa_CNL.jpg

17_11aPolypMedusa_CL.jpg

17_11aPolypMedusa_CNL.jpg

17_11bPolypMedusa_CL.jpg

17_11bPolypMedusa_CNL.jpg

17_11ax1CorlPolyps_XUP.jpg

17_11ax2SeaAnem_XUP.jpg

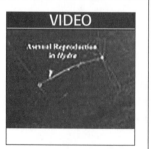

17_11aHydraBudding_SV.mpg

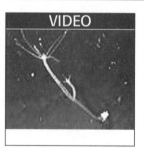

17_11aHydraBudding_VT.swf

17_11aHydraEating_SV.mpg

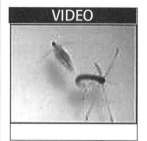

17_11aHydraEating_VT.swf

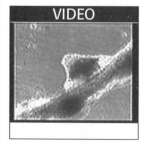

17_11aHydraSperm_SV.mpg

17_11aHydraSperm_VT.swf

VIDEO

17_11bJellySwimming_SV.mpg

VIDEO

17_11bJellySwimming_VT.swf

VIDEO

17_11bThimbleJellies_SV.mpg

VIDEO

17_11bThimbleJellies_VT.swf

VIDEO

17_11CoralReef_SV.mpg

VIDEO

17_11CoralReef_VT.swf

17_11bx1PurpStrpJel_XUP.jpg

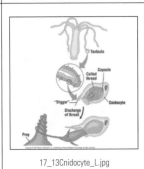

17_11bx2LionMnJelly_XUP.jpg

17_11x1Cnidarians_XUP.jpg

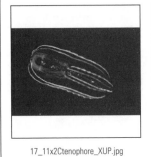

17_11x2Ctenophore_XUP.jpg

17_12CoralAnimals_UP.jpg

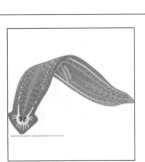

17_13Cnidocyte_L.jpg

17_13Cnidocyte_U.jpg

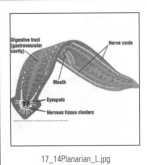

17_14Planarian_L.jpg

17_14Planarian_U.jpg

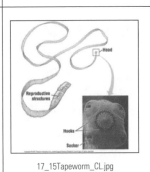

17_15Tapeworm_CL.jpg

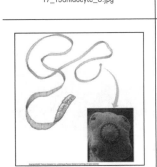

17_15Tapeworm_CNL.jpg

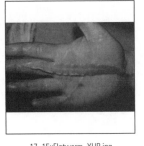

17_15xFlatworm_XUP.jpg

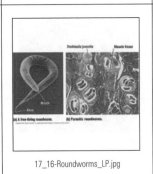

17_16-Roundworms_LP.jpg

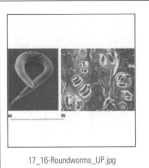

17_16-Roundworms_UP.jpg

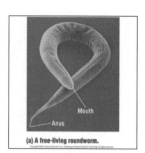

17_16aRoundworm_LP.jpg

17_16aRoundworm_UP.jpg

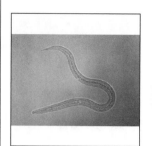

17_16axNematCElegans_XUP.jpg

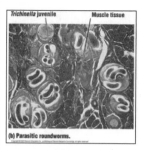

17_16bTrichinell_LP.jpg

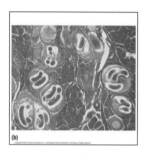

17_16bTrichinell_UP.jpg

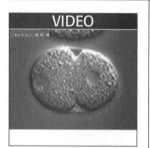

17_16CElegansCrawl_SV.mpg

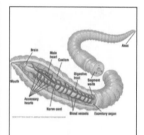

17_16CElegansCrawl_VT.swf

17_16CElegansEmbryo_SV.mpg

17_16CElegansEmbryo_VT.swf

17_17Earthworm_L.jpg

17_17Earthworm_U.jpg

17_17EarthwormLocomot_SV.mpg

17_17EarthwormLocomot_VT.swf

17_17xEarthworm_XUP.jpg

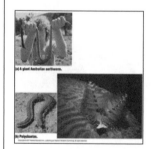

17_18-Annelids_LP.jpg

17_18-Annelids_UP.jpg

17_18aAnnelids_LP.jpg

17_18aAnnelids_UP.jpg

17_18b-Annelids_LP.jpg

17_18b-Annelids_UP.jpg

17_18b1Annelids_UP.jpg

17_18b2Annelids_UP.jpg

17_18bTubeworms_SV.mpg

17_18bTubeworms_VT.swf

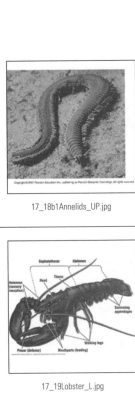

17_19Lobster_L.jpg

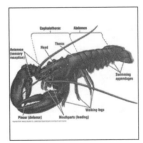

17_19Lobster_U.jpg

17_19LobsterMouthParts_SV.mpg

17_19LobsterMouthParts_VT.swf

17_20-Arachnids_LP.jpg

17_20-Arachnids_UP.jpg

17_20aArachnids_LP.jpg

17_20aArachnids_UP.jpg

17_20bArachnids_LP.jpg

17_20bArachnids_UP.jpg

17_20cArachnids_LP.jpg

17_20cArachnids_UP.jpg

17_21-Crustaceans_LP.jpg

17_21-Crustaceans_UP.jpg

17_21aCrustaceans_LP.jpg

17_21aCrustaceans_UP.jpg

17_21bCrustaceans_LP.jpg

17_21bCrustaceans_UP.jpg

17_22Millipede_UP.jpg

17_23-InsectDiversity_LP.jpg

17_23-InsectDiversity_UP.jpg

17_23aInsectDiversity_LP.jpg

17_23aInsectDiversity_UP.jpg

17_23bInsectDiversity_LP.jpg

17_23bInsectDiversity_UP.jpg

17_23cInsectDiversity_LP.jpg

17_23cInsectDiversity_UP.jpg

17_23cxBeetle_XUP.jpg

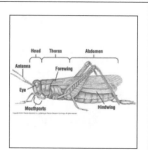

17_24Grasshopper_L.jpg

17_24Grasshopper_U.jpg

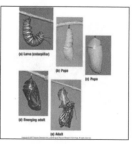

17_25-Metamorphosis_LP.jpg

17_25-Metamorphosis_UP.jpg

17_25aMetamorphosis_LP.jpg

17_25aMetamorphosis_UP.jpg

17_25bMetamorphosis_LP.jpg

17_25bMetamorphosis_UP.jpg

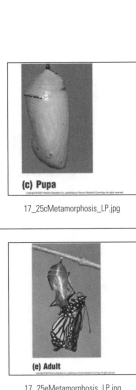

(c) Pupa

17_25cMetamorphosis_LP.jpg

(c)

17_25cMetamorphosis_UP.jpg

(d) Emerging adult

17_25dMetamorphosis_LP.jpg

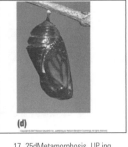

(d)

17_25dMetamorphosis_UP.jpg

(e) Adult

17_25eMetamorphosis_LP.jpg

(e)

17_25eMetamorphosis_UP.jpg

VIDEO

17_25ButterflyEmerge_SV.mpg

VIDEO

17_25ButterflyEmerge_VT.swf

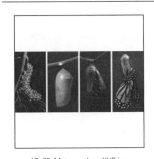

17_25xMetamorphos_XUP.jpg

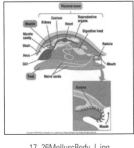

17_26MolluscBody_L.jpg

17_26MolluscBody_U.jpg

17_27-Molluscs_LP.jpg

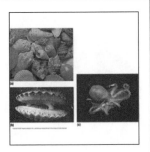

17_27-Molluscs_UP.jpg

(a) Gastropod shells.

17_27aMolluscs_LP.jpg

(a)

17_27aMolluscs_UP.jpg

(b) A bivalve.

17_27bMolluscs_LP.jpg

(b)

17_27bMolluscs_UP.jpg

(c) A cephalopod.

17_27cMolluscs_LP.jpg

(c)

17_27cMolluscs_UP.jpg

VIDEO

17_27aNudibranchs_SV.mpg

17_27aNudibranchs_VT.swf

17_28-Echinoderms_LP.jpg

17_28-Echinoderms_UP.jpg

17_28a-Echinoderms_LP.jpg

17_28a-Echinoderms_UP.jpg

17_28a1Echinoderms_UP.jpg

17_28a2Echinoderms_UP.jpg

17_28aEchinodermTubeFee_SV.mpg

17_28aEchinodermTubeFee_VT.swf

17_28ax1Bloodstar_XUP.jpg

17_28ax2BrittleStar_XUP.jpg

17_28bEchinoderms_LP.jpg

17_28bEchinoderms_UP.jpg

17_28cEchinoderms_LP.jpg

17_28cEchinoderms_UP.jpg

17_29SnakeVertebrae_UP.jpg

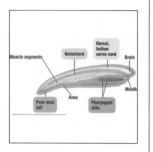

17_30Chordate_L.jpg

17_30Chordate_U.jpg

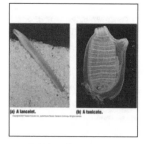

17_31-InvertChordates_LP.jpg

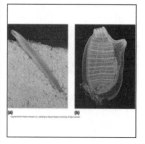

17_31-InvertChordates_UP.jpg

(a) A lancelet.

17_31aInvertChordates_LP.jpg

(a)

17_31aInvertChordates_UP.jpg

(b) A tunicate.

17_31bInvertChordates_LP.jpg

(b)

17_31bInvertChordates_UP.jpg

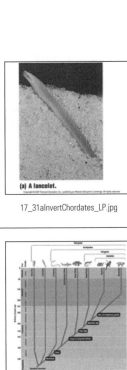

17_32VertebratePhyl_L.jpg

17_32VertebratePhyl_U.jpg

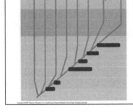

17_33-FishDiversity_LP.jpg

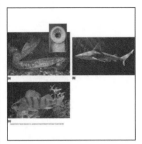

17_33-FishDiversity_UP.jpg

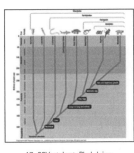

(a) A sea lamprey (the inset shows its rasping mouth)

17_33aFishDiversity_LP.jpg

17_33aFishDiversity_UP.jpg

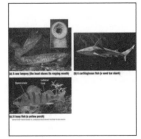

(b) A cartilaginous fish (a sand bar shark)

17_33bFishDiversity_LP.jpg

(b)

17_33bFishDiversity_UP.jpg

17_33bxCartilFishes_XUP.jpg

Operculum | Lateral line

(c) A bony fish (a yellow perch)

17_33cFishDiversity_LP.jpg

(c)

17_33cFishDiversity_UP.jpg

VIDEO

17_33bMantaRay_SV.mpg

VIDEO

17_33bMantaRay_VT.swf

VIDEO

17_33bSharkEatSeal_SV.mpg

VIDEO

17_33bSharkEatSeal_VT.swf

VIDEO

17_33cClownfishAnemone_SV.mpg

17_33cClownfishAnemone_VT.swf

17_34-DualLife_LP.jpg

17_34-DualLife_UP.jpg

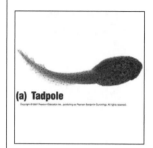

17_34aTadpole_LP.jpg

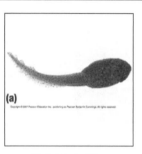

17_34aTadpole_UP.jpg

17_34bTadpoleMetamorph_LP.jpg

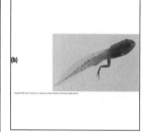

17_34bTadpoleMetamorph_UP.jpg

17_34cAdultFrog_LP.jpg

17_34cAdultFrog_UP.jpg

17_35TetrapodOrigin_L.jpg

17_35TetrapodOrigin_U.jpg

17_36BullSnake_UP.jpg

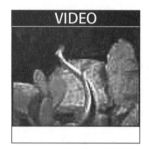

17_36SnakesWrestle_SV.mpg

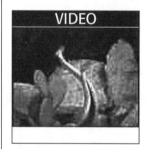

17_36SnakesWrestle_VT.swf

17_36Tortoise_SV.mpg

17_36Tortoise_VT.swf

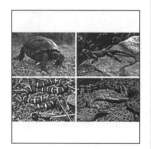

17_36x1ExtantReptiles_XUP.jpg

17_36x2DesertTortoise_XUP.jpg

17_36x3LizardOnRock_XUP.jpg

17_36x4KingSnake_XUP.jpg

17_36x5Alligators_XUP.jpg

17_36x6SeaTurtle_XUP.jpg

17_36x7BandedGecko_XUP.jpg

17_36x8EmerTreeBoa_XUP.jpg

17_36x9Newt_XUP.jpg

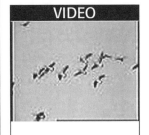

17_37MesozoicFeed_L.jpg

17_38Airfoil_CL.jpg

17_38Airfoil_CNL.jpg

17_38FlappingGeese_SV.mpg

17_38FlappingGeese_VT.swf

17_38SoaringHawk_SV.mpg

17_38SoaringHawk_VT.swf

17_38SwansTakeFlight_SV.mpg

17_38SwansTakeFlight_VT.swf

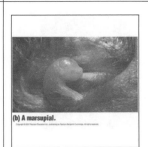

17_38xPenguins_XUP.jpg

17_39-MammalGroups_LP.jpg

17_39-MammalGroups_UP.jpg

17_39aMammalGroups_LP.jpg

17_39aMammalGroups_UP.jpg

17_39bMammalGroups_LP.jpg

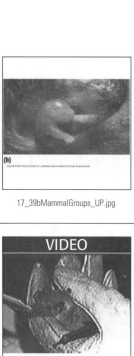

17_39bMammalGroups_UP.jpg

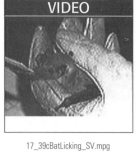

17_39bxMarsupMouse_XUP.jpg

17_39cMammalGroups_LP.jpg

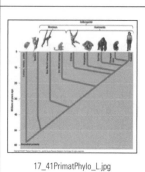

17_39cMammalGroups_UP.jpg

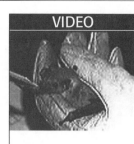

17_39cBatLicking_SV.mpg

17_39cBatLicking_VT.swf

17_40Orangutan_UP.jpg

17_41PrimatPhylo_L.jpg

17_41PrimatPhylo_U.jpg

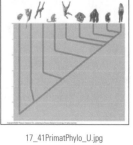

17_42-PrimatDiversity1_LP.jpg

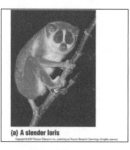

17_42-PrimatDiversity1_UP.jpg

17_42-PrimatDiversity2_LP.jpg

17_42-PrimatDiversity2_UP.jpg

17_42aPrimatDiversity_LP.jpg

17_42aPrimatDiversity_UP.jpg

17_42axLemurs_XUP.jpg

17_42bPrimatDiversity_LP.jpg

17_42bPrimatDiversity_UP.jpg

17_42c-PrimatDiversity_LP.jpg

17_42c-PrimatDiversity_UP.jpg

17_42c1PrimatDiversity_UP.jpg

17_42c2PrimatDiversity_UP.jpg

17_42cxOldNewMonkey_XUP.jpg

17_42d-PrimatDiversity_LP.jpg

17_42d-PrimatDiversity_UP.jpg

17_42d1PrimatDiversity_UP.jpg

17_42d2PrimatDiversity_UP.jpg

17_42d3PrimatDiversity_UP.jpg

17_42d4PrimatDiversity_UP.jpg

17_42dxApesCollage_XUP.jpg

(e) A human with young (hominoids)

17_42ePrimatDiversity_LP.jpg

(e)

17_42ePrimatDiversity_UP.jpg

VIDEO

17_42dChimpAgonistic_SV.mpg

VIDEO

17_42dChimpAgonistic_VT.swf

VIDEO

17_42dChimpCrackNut_SV.mpg

VIDEO

17_42dChimpCrackNut_VT.swf

VIDEO

17_42dGibbonBrachiating_SV.mpg

VIDEO

17_42dGibbonBrachiating_VT.swf

VIDEO

17_42dWolvesAgonistic_SV.mpg

VIDEO

17_42dWolvesAgonistic_VT.swf

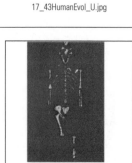

17_43HumanEvol_L.jpg

17_43HumanEvol_U.jpg

17_44-UprightPosture_LP.jpg

17_44-UprightPosture_UP.jpg

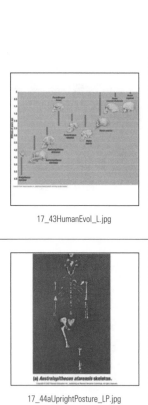

17_44aUprightPosture_LP.jpg

17_44aUprightPosture_UP.jpg

17_44bUprightPosture_LP.jpg

17_44bUprightPosture_UP.jpg

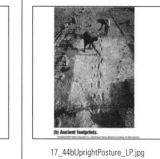

17_44cUprightPosture_LP.jpg

17_44cUprightPosture_UP.jpg

17_45-ArtHistory_LP.jpg

17_45-ArtHistory_UP.jpg

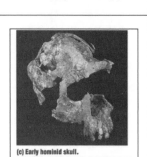
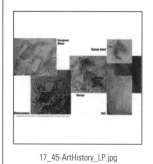
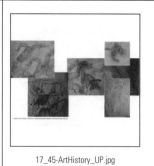

17_45aArtHistory_UP.jpg

17_45bArtHistory_UP.jpg

17_45cArtHistory_UP.jpg

17_45dArtHistory_UP.jpg

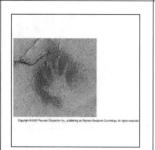

17_45eArtHistory_UP.jpg

17_46ClearCutForest_UP.jpg

17_46x1Deforestation _XUP.jpg

17_46x2SlashBurn_XUP.jpg

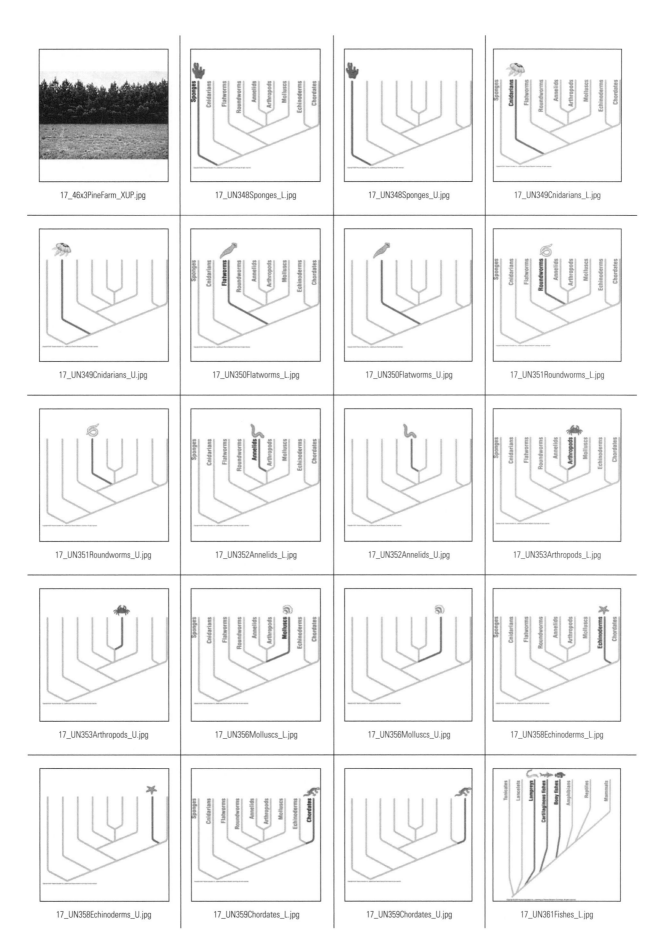

17_46x3PineFarm_XUP.jpg

17_UN348Sponges_L.jpg

17_UN348Sponges_U.jpg

17_UN349Cnidarians_L.jpg

17_UN349Cnidarians_U.jpg

17_UN350Flatworms_L.jpg

17_UN350Flatworms_U.jpg

17_UN351Roundworms_L.jpg

17_UN351Roundworms_U.jpg

17_UN352Annelids_L.jpg

17_UN352Annelids_U.jpg

17_UN353Arthropods_L.jpg

17_UN353Arthropods_U.jpg

17_UN356Molluscs_L.jpg

17_UN356Molluscs_U.jpg

17_UN358Echinoderms_L.jpg

17_UN358Echinoderms_U.jpg

17_UN359Chordates_L.jpg

17_UN359Chordates_U.jpg

17_UN361Fishes_L.jpg

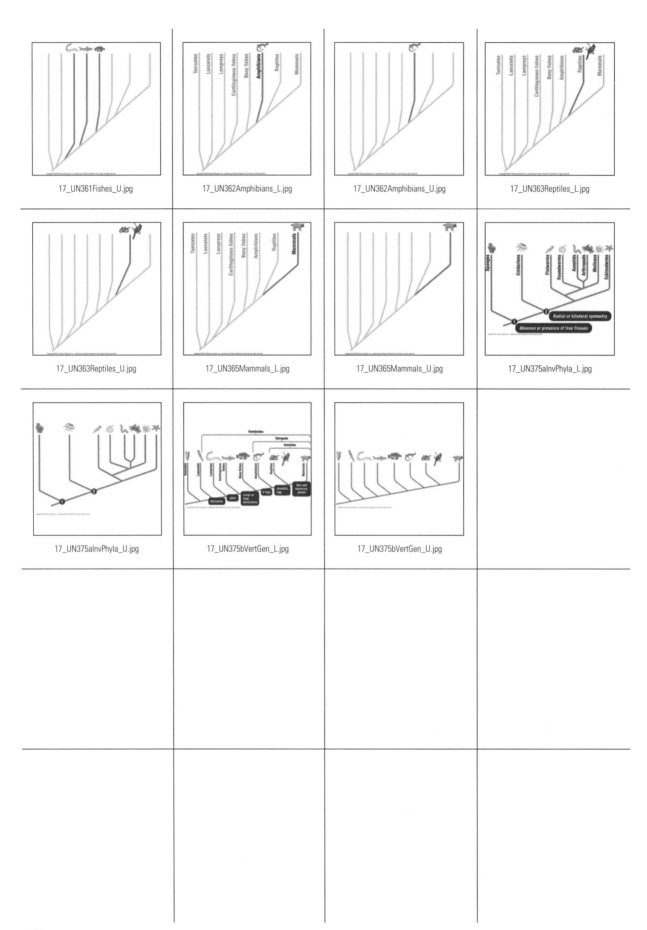

17_UN361Fishes_U.jpg

17_UN362Amphibians_L.jpg

17_UN362Amphibians_U.jpg

17_UN363Reptiles_L.jpg

17_UN363Reptiles_U.jpg

17_UN365Mammals_L.jpg

17_UN365Mammals_U.jpg

17_UN375aInvPhyla_L.jpg

17_UN375aInvPhyla_U.jpg

17_UN375bVertGen_L.jpg

17_UN375bVertGen_U.jpg

Chapter 18 The Ecology of Organisms and Populations

18_00aUrbanCrowd_LP.jpg

18_00bForestFire_LP.jpg

18_00cMountaineering_LP.jpg

18_00dExtinctBird_LP.jpg

18_01HumanImpact_UP.jpg

18_02-ForestCanopy_LP.jpg

18_02-ForestCanopy_UP.jpg

18_02aForestCanopy_LP.jpg

18_02aForestCanopy_UP.jpg

18_02bForestCanopy_LP.jpg

18_02bForestCanopy_UP.jpg

18_03-Ecology_LP.jpg

18_03-Ecology_UP.jpg

18_03aEcology_LP.jpg

18_03aEcology_UP.jpg

18_03bEcology_LP.jpg

18_03bEcology_UP.jpg

18_03cEcology_LP.jpg

18_03cEcology_UP.jpg

18_03dEcology_LP.jpg

18_03dEcology_UP.jpg

18_04RachelCarson_UP.jpg

18_05EnvironActivism_UP.jpg

18_06GlobalProduct_UP.jpg

18_07Patchiness_UP.jpg

18_08HotProkPool_UP.jpg

18_09FlaggingTrees_UP.jpg

18_10-ForestFire_UP.jpg

18_10aForestFire_UP.jpg

18_10bForestFire_UP.jpg

18_10x1MtStHelens_XUP.jpg

18_10x2MtStHelens_XUP.jpg

18_11LizardBiog_L.jpg

18_11LizardBiog_U.jpg

18_12WinterStorm_UP.jpg

18_13PrairieDogs_UP.jpg

18_14MarkRecapture_UP.jpg

18_15-Dispersion_CL.jpg

18_15-Dispersion_CNL.jpg

18_15aDispersion_CL.jpg

18_15aDispersion_CNL.jpg

18_15bDispersion_CL.jpg

18_15bDispersion_CNL.jpg

18_15cDispersion_CL.jpg

18_15cDispersion_CNL.jpg

18_15aFlappingGeese_SV.mpg

18_15aFlappingGeese_VT.swf

18_15bAlbatrossCourtshi_SV.mpg

18_15bAlbatrossCourtshi_VT.swf

18_15cSalmonellaFlagell_SV.mpg

18_15cSalmonellaFlagell_VT.swf

18_15axClumpedCollage_XUP.jpg

18_15bxUniform_XUP.jpg

18_15cxRandomFerns_XUP.jpg

18_16DifferentScales_LP.jpg

18_16DifferentScales_UP.jpg

18_17-ExpGrowth_L.jpg

18_17-ExpGrowth_U.jpg

18_17aExpGrowth_L.jpg

18_17aExpGrowth_U.jpg

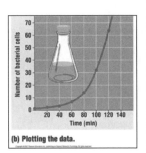

18_17bExpGrowth_L.jpg

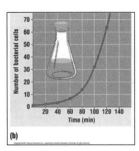

18_17bExpGrowth_U.jpg

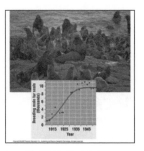

18_18FurSealGrowth_CL.jpg

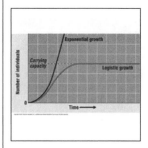

18_19GrowCurves_L.jpg

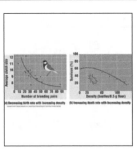

18_20-DensityDependent_L.jpg

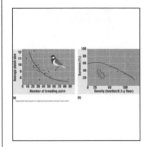

18_20-DensityDependent_U.jpg

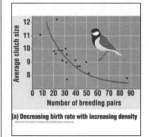

18_20aDensityDependent_L.jpg

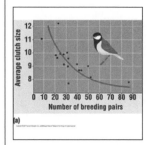

18_20aDensityDependent_U.jpg

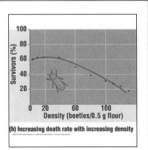

18_20bDensityDependent_L.jpg

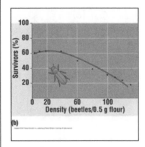

18_20bDensityDependent_U.jpg

18_21TwinFawns_UP.jpg

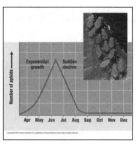

18_22AphidPopulation_CL.jpg

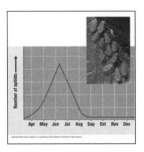

18_22AphidPopulation_CNL.jpg

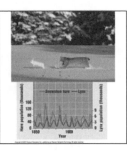

18_23-PopulationCycles_CL.jpg

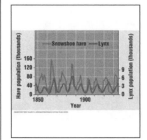

18_23aPopulationCycles_L.jpg

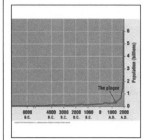

18_24HumPopGrowGraph_L.jpg

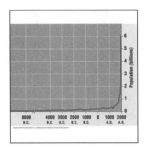

18_24HumPopGrowGraph_U.jpg

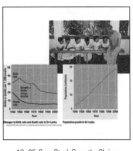

18_25-CaseStudyGrowth_CL.jpg

18_25aCaseStudyGrowth_UP.jpg

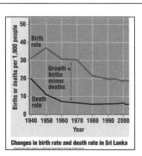

18_25bCaseStudyGrowth_L.jpg

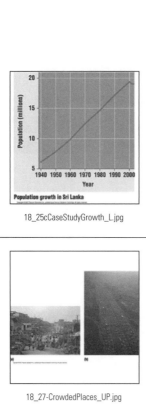

18_25cCaseStudyGrowth_L.jpg

18_26AgeStructures_L.jpg

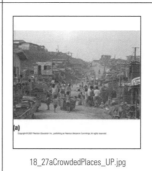

18_26AgeStructures_U.jpg

18_27-CrowdedPlaces_LP.jpg

18_27-CrowdedPlaces_UP.jpg

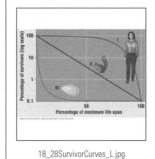

18_27aCrowdedPlaces_LP.jpg

18_27aCrowdedPlaces_UP.jpg

18_27bCrowdedPlaces_LP.jpg

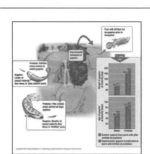

18_27bCrowdedPlaces_UP.jpg

18_28SurvivorCurves_L.jpg

18_29CenturyPlant_UP.jpg

18_30DavidResnick_UP.jpg

18_31TestDarwinHyp_L.jpg

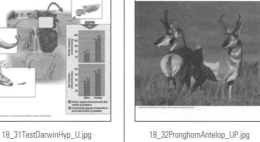

18_31TestDarwinHyp_U.jpg

18_32PronghornAntelop_UP.jpg

18_32aDucklings_SV.mpg

18_32aDucklings_VT.swf

18_32bChimpCrackNut_SV.mpg

18_32bChimpCrackNut_VT.swf

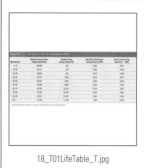

18_T01LifeTable_T.jpg

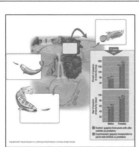

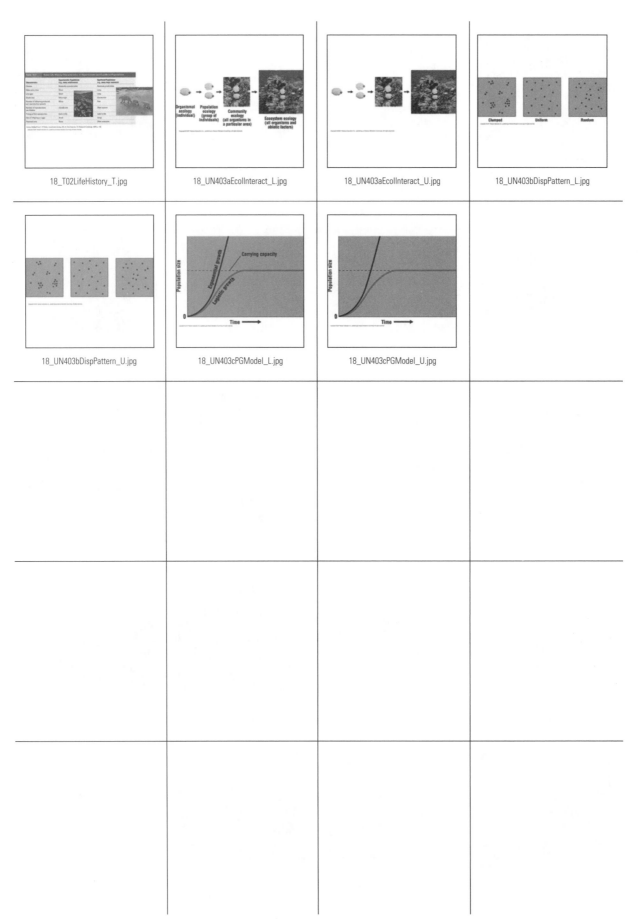

18_T02LifeHistory_T.jpg

18_UN403aEcolInteract_L.jpg

18_UN403aEcolInteract_U.jpg

18_UN403bDispPattern_L.jpg

18_UN403bDispPattern_U.jpg

18_UN403cPGModel_L.jpg

18_UN403cPGModel_U.jpg

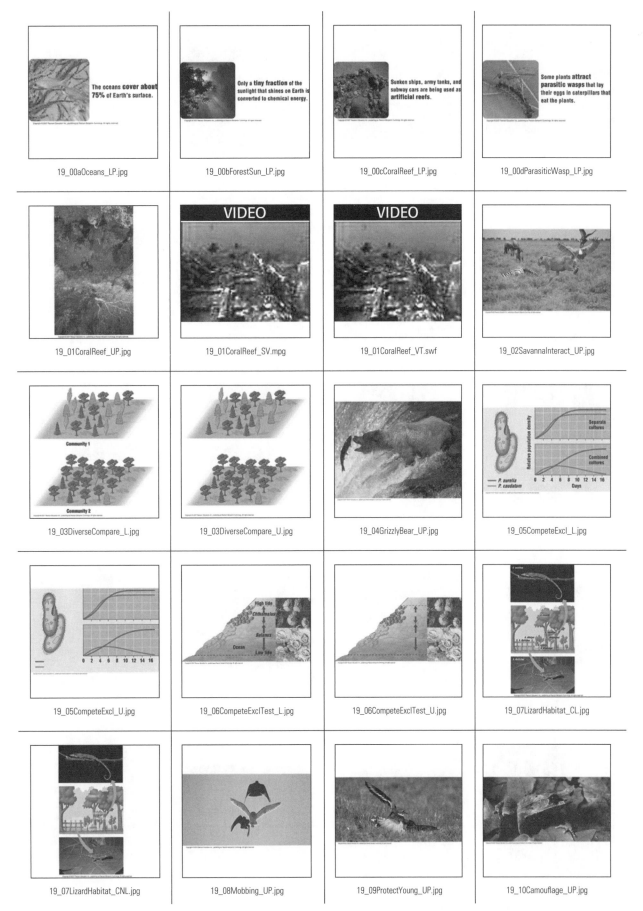

19_00aOceans_LP.jpg

19_00bForestSun_LP.jpg

19_00cCoralReef_LP.jpg

19_00dParasiticWasp_LP.jpg

19_01CoralReef_UP.jpg

19_01CoralReef_SV.mpg

19_01CoralReef_VT.swf

19_02SavannaInteract_UP.jpg

19_03DiverseCompare_L.jpg

19_03DiverseCompare_U.jpg

19_04GrizzlyBear_UP.jpg

19_05CompeteExcl_L.jpg

19_05CompeteExcl_U.jpg

19_06CompeteExclTest_L.jpg

19_06CompeteExclTest_U.jpg

19_07LizardHabitat_CL.jpg

19_07LizardHabitat_CNL.jpg

19_08Mobbing_UP.jpg

19_09ProtectYoung_UP.jpg

19_10Camouflage_UP.jpg

19_10SeaHorses_SV.mpg

19_10SeaHorses_VT.swf

19_11WarningColor_UP.jpg

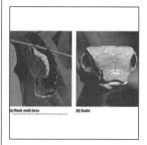

19_12-BatesianMimicry_LP.jpg

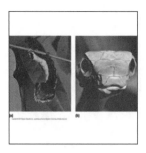

19_12-BatesianMimicry_UP.jpg

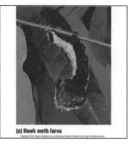

19_12aBatesianMimicry_LP.jpg

19_12aBatesianMimicry_UP.jpg

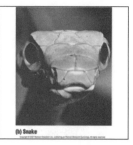

19_12bBatesianMimicry_LP.jpg

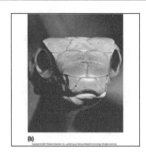

19_12bBatesianMimicry_UP.jpg

19_13-MullerianMimicry_LP.jpg

19_13-MullerianMimicry_UP.jpg

19_13aMullerianMimicry_LP.jpg

19_13aMullerianMimicry_UP.jpg

19_13bMullerianMimicry_LP.jpg

19_13bMullerianMimicry_UP.jpg

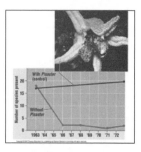

19_14KeystonePred_CL.jpg

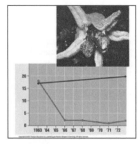

19_14KeystonePred_CNL.jpg

19_15AustralRabbits_UP.jpg

19_16AcaciaAnts_UP.jpg

19_16ClownfishAnemone_SV.mpg

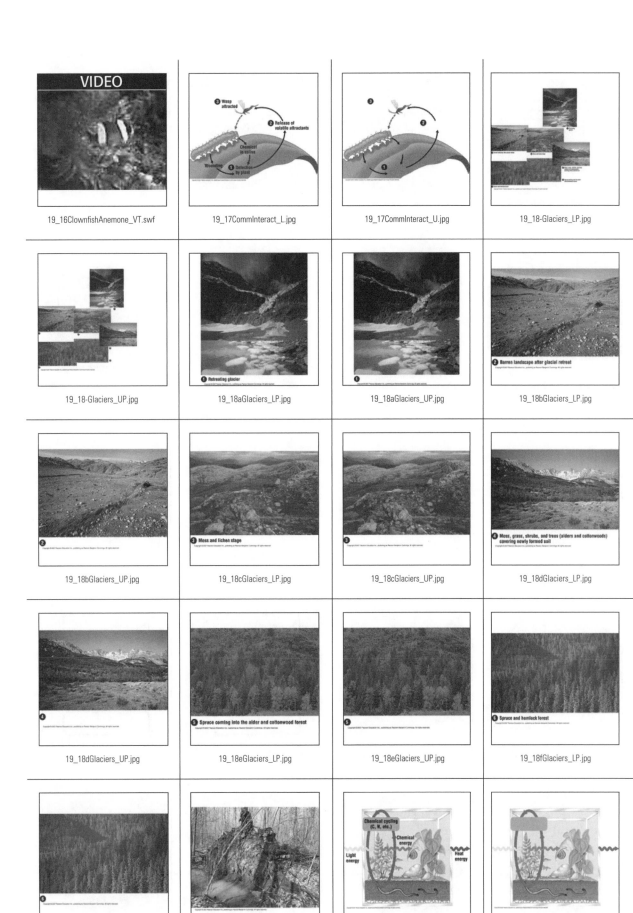

VIDEO

19_16ClownfishAnemone_VT.swf

19_17CommInteract_L.jpg

19_17CommInteract_U.jpg

19_18-Glaciers_LP.jpg

19_18-Glaciers_UP.jpg

19_18aGlaciers_LP.jpg

19_18aGlaciers_UP.jpg

19_18bGlaciers_LP.jpg

19_18bGlaciers_UP.jpg

19_18cGlaciers_LP.jpg

19_18cGlaciers_UP.jpg

19_18dGlaciers_LP.jpg

19_18dGlaciers_UP.jpg

19_18eGlaciers_LP.jpg

19_18eGlaciers_UP.jpg

19_18fGlaciers_LP.jpg

19_18fGlaciers_UP.jpg

19_19WindDisturbance_UP.jpg

19_20TerrariumEco_L.jpg

19_20TerrariumEco_U.jpg

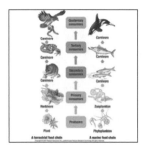

19_21FoodChain_L.jpg

19_21FoodChain_U.jpg

19_21SharkEatSeal_SV.mpg

19_21SharkEatSeal_VT.swf

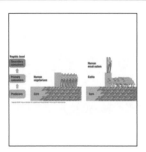

19_22RottingLog_UP.jpg

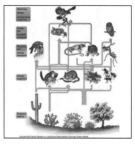

19_23FoodWeb_L.jpg

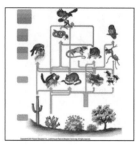

19_23FoodWeb_U.jpg

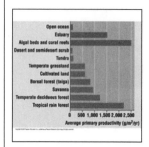

19_24BiomeProd_L.jpg

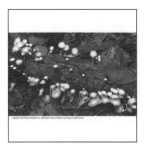

19_25EnergyLoss_L.jpg

19_25EnergyLoss_U.jpg

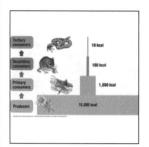

19_26EnergyPyramid_L.jpg

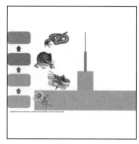

19_26EnergyPyramid_U.jpg

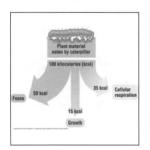

19_27HumanEnergyPyr_L.jpg

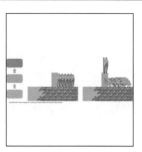

19_27HumanEnergyPyr_U.jpg

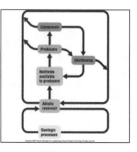

19_28Biogeochem_L.jpg

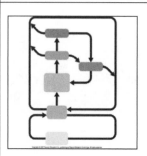

19_28Biogeochem_U.jpg

19_29aCarbonCycle_L.jpg

19_29aCarbonCycle_U.jpg

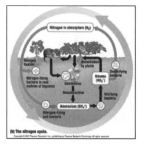

19_29bNitroCycle_L.jpg

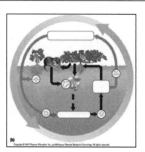

19_29bNitroCycle_U.jpg

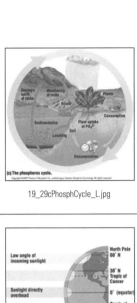

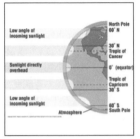

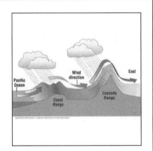

19_29cPhosphCycle_L.jpg

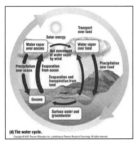

19_29cPhosphCycle_U.jpg

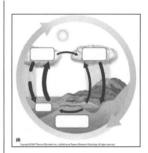

19_29dWaterCycle_L.jpg

19_29dWaterCycle_U.jpg

19_30SolarRadiation_L.jpg

19_30SolarRadiation_U.jpg

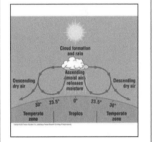

19_31RainWindEffect_L.jpg

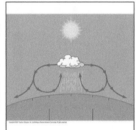

19_31RainWindEffect_U.jpg

19_32RainShadow_L.jpg

19_32RainShadow_U.jpg

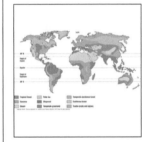

19_33Biomes_L.jpg

19_33Biomes_U.jpg

19_34aTropicalForest_CL.jpg

19_34aTropicalForest_CNL.jpg

19_34bSavanna_CL.jpg

19_34bSavanna_CNL.jpg

19_34cDesert_CL.jpg

19_34cDesert_CNL.jpg

19_34dChaparral_CL.jpg

19_34dChaparral_CNL.jpg

(e) Temperate grassland.

19_34eGrassland_CL.jpg

(e)

19_34eGrassland_CNL.jpg

(f) Temperate deciduous forest.

19_34fDeciduous_CL.jpg

(f)

19_34fDeciduous_CNL.jpg

(g) Coniferous forest.

19_34gConiferous_CL.jpg

(g)

19_34gConiferous_CNL.jpg

(h) Tundra.

19_34hTundra_CL.jpg

(h)

19_34hTundra_CNL.jpg

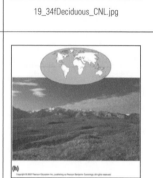

19_35-FreshwatBiomes_LP.jpg

19_35-FreshwatBiomes_UP.jpg

(a) Satellite view of the Great lakes

19_35aFreshwatBiomes_LP.jpg

(a)

19_35aFreshwatBiomes_UP.jpg

(b) A stream in the Great Smoky Mountains, Tennessee

19_35bFreshwatBiomes_LP.jpg

(b)

19_35bFreshwatBiomes_UP.jpg

(c) A freshwater wetland in Georgia

19_35cFreshwatBiomes_LP.jpg

(c)

19_35cFreshwatBiomes_UP.jpg

19_36-RiverBasin_CL.jpg

19_36-RiverBasin_CNL.jpg

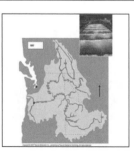

19_36aRiverBasin_L.jpg

19_36aRiverBasin_U.jpg

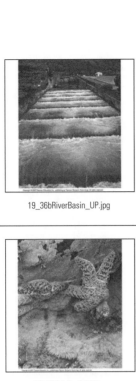

19_36bRiverBasin_UP.jpg

19_37Estuary_UP.jpg

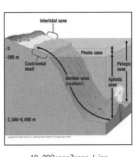

19_38OceanZones_L.jpg

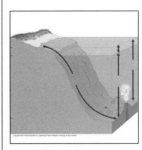

19_38OceanZones_U.jpg

19_39TidePool_UP.jpg

19_40-UnderseaVent_UP.jpg

19_40aUnderseaVent_UP.jpg

19_40bUnderseaVent_UP.jpg

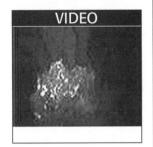

19_40HydrothermalVent_SV.mpg

19_40HydrothermalVent_VT.swf

19_40Tubeworms_SV.mpg

19_40Tubeworms_VT.swf

19_41-Coevolution_LP.jpg

19_41-Coevolution_UP.jpg

19_41aCoevolution_LP.jpg

19_41aCoevolution_UP.jpg

19_41bCoevolution_LP.jpg

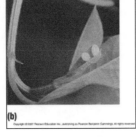

19_41bCoevolution_UP.jpg

19_41cPassionFlower_LP.jpg

19_41cPassionFlower_UP.jpg

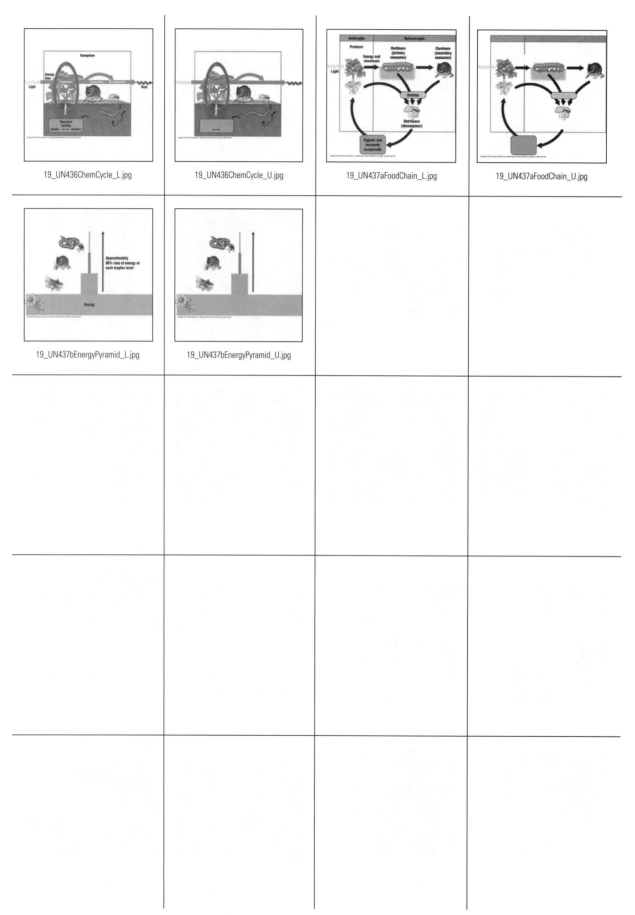

19_UN436ChemCycle_L.jpg

19_UN436ChemCycle_U.jpg

19_UN437aFoodChain_L.jpg

19_UN437aFoodChain_U.jpg

19_UN437bEnergyPyramid_L.jpg

19_UN437bEnergyPyramid_U.jpg

Chapter 20 Human Impact on the Environment

20_00aEagle_LP.jpg

20_00bLemurs_LP.jpg

20_00cShoppingCart_LP.jpg

20_00dRainForest_LP.jpg

20_01-NonNative_LP.jpg

20_01-NonNative_UP.jpg

20_01aNonNative_LP.jpg

20_01aNonNative_UP.jpg

20_01bNonNative_LP.jpg

20_01bNonNative_UP.jpg

20_02OpenPitMine_UP.jpg

20_03-IntroducedSpecies_LP.jpg

20_03-IntroducedSpecies_UP.jpg

20_03aIntroducedSpecies_LP.jpg

20_03aIntroducedSpecies_UP.jpg

20_03bIntroducedSpecies_LP.jpg

20_03bIntroducedSpecies_UP.jpg

20_03cIntroducedSpecies_LP.jpg

20_03cIntroducedSpecies_UP.jpg

20_03dIntroducedSpecies_LP.jpg

20_03dIntroducedSpecies_UP.jpg

20_04CO2Producers_UP.jpg

20_05Eutrophication_UP.jpg

20_06Deforestation_UP.jpg

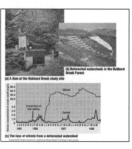

20_07-HubbardBrookStdy_CL.jpg

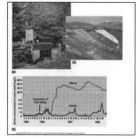

20_07-HubbardBrookStdy_CNL.jpg

20_07aHubbardBrookStdy_LP.jpg

20_07aHubbardBrookStdy_UP.jpg

20_07bHubbardBrookStdy_LP.jpg

20_07bHubbardBrookStdy_UP.jpg

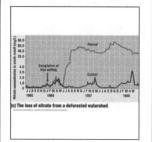

20_07cHubbardBrookStdy_L.jpg

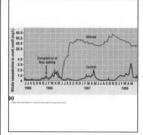

20_07cHubbardBrookStdy_U.jpg

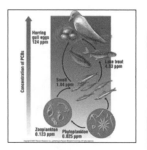

20_08Biomagnific_L.jpg

20_08Biomagnific_U.jpg

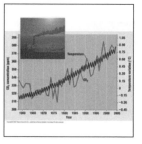

20_09Earthrise_UP.jpg

20_10CO2GraphSmokstac_CL.jpg

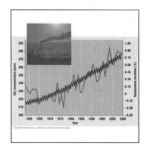

20_10CO2GraphSmokstac_CNL.jpg

20_11Greenhouse_L.jpg

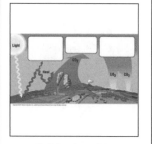

20_11Greenhouse_U.jpg

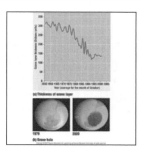

20_12-OzoneShield_CL.jpg

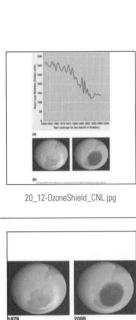

20_12-OzoneShield_CNL.jpg

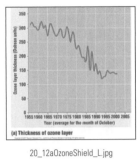

20_12aOzoneShield_L.jpg

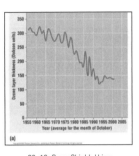

20_12aOzoneShield_U.jpg

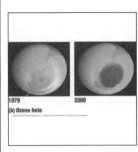

20_12bOzoneShield_L.jpg

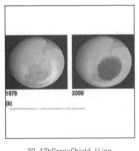

20_12bOzoneShield_U.jpg

20_13RainForest_UP.jpg

20_14-HundredHeartbeat_LP.jpg

20_14-HundredHeartbeat_UP.jpg

20_14aHundredHeartbeat_LP.jpg

20_14aHundredHeartbeat_UP.jpg

20_14bHundredHeartbeat_LP.jpg

20_14bHundredHeartbeat_UP.jpg

20_14cHundredHeartbeat_LP.jpg

20_14cHundredHeartbeat_UP.jpg

20_15-BiodiversityCrisis_LP.jpg

20_15-BiodiversityCrisis_UP.jpg

20_15aBiodiversityCrisis_LP.jpg

20_15aBiodiversityCrisis_UP.jpg

20_15bBiodiversityCrisis_LP.jpg

20_15bBiodiversityCrisis_UP.jpg

20_15cBiodiversityCrisis_LP.jpg

20_15cBiodiversityCrisis_UP.jpg

20_16RosyPeriwinkle_UP.jpg

20_17HotSpots_L.jpg

20_18-Fragmentation_LP.jpg

20_18aFragmentation_LP.jpg

20_18bFragmentation_UP.jpg

20_19-HabitatRequirement_LP.jpg

20_19-HabitatRequirement_UP.jpg

20_19aHabitatRequirement_LP.jpg

20_19aHabitatRequirement_UP.jpg

20_19bHabitatRequirement_LP.jpg

20_19bHabitatRequirement_UP.jpg

20_19cHabitatRequirement_LP.jpg

20_19cHabitatRequirement_UP.jpg

20_20-LandscapeEdges_LP.jpg

20_20-LandscapeEdges_UP.jpg

20_20aLandscapeEdges_LP.jpg

20_20aLandscapeEdges_UP.jpg

20_20bLandscapeEdges_LP.jpg

20_20bLandscapeEdges_UP.jpg

20_21HumanCorridor_UP.jpg

20_22-ZonedReserves_CNL.jpg

20_22aZonedReserves_L.jpg

20_22bZonedReserves_UP.jpg

20_23EOWilson_LP.jpg

20_24Biophilia_LP.jpg

20_T01Sustainability_T.jpg

20_UN461aPCBconcentrat_L.jpg

20_UN461aPCBconcentrat_U.jpg

20_UN461bBiodiversLevel_L.jpg

20_UN461bBiodiversLevel_U.jpg

20_UN461cBioCrisis_L.jpg

20_UN461cBioCrisis_U.jpg

Chapter 21 Unifying Concepts of Animal Structure and Function

21_00aNeuron_LP.jpg

21_00bPiercing_LP.jpg

21_00cHibernation_LP.jpg

21_00dHotTub_LP.jpg

21_01SweatBeckham_UP.jpg

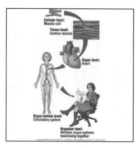

21_02StructureHierarchy_L.jpg

21_02StructureHierarchy_U.jpg

21_03-FormFitsFunction_LP.jpg

21_03-FormFitsFunction_UP.jpg

21_03aFormFitsFunction_UP.jpg

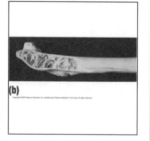

21_03bFormFitsFunction_UP.jpg

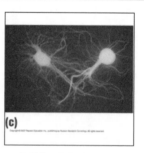

21_03cFormFitsFunction_UP.jpg

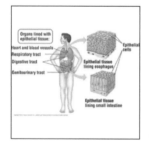

21_04_EpithelialTissue_L.jpg

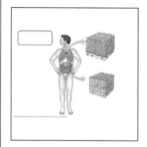

21_04_EpithelialTissue_U.jpg

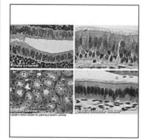

21_04x1EpithelialTissue_XLP.jpg

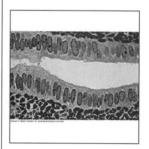

21_04x2SimpleColumn_XUP.jpg

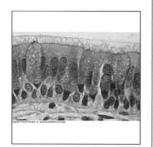

21_04x3Pseudostratd_XUP.jpg

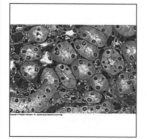

21_04x4SimpleCuboid_XUP.jpg

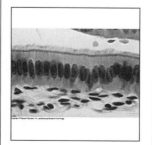

21_04x5ColumnrCiliat_XUP.jpg

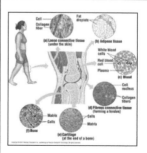

21_05-ConnTissue_CL.jpg

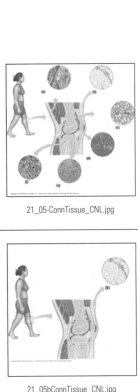

21_05-ConnTissue_CNL.jpg

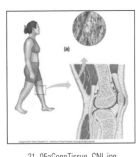

21_05aConnTissue_CL.jpg

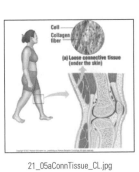

21_05aConnTissue_CNL.jpg

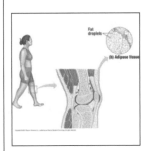

21_05bConnTissue_CL.jpg

21_05bConnTissue_CNL.jpg

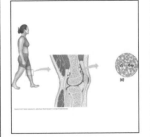

21_05cConnTissue_CL.jpg

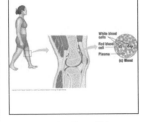

21_05cConnTissue_CNL.jpg

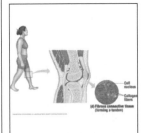

21_05dConnTissue_CL.jpg

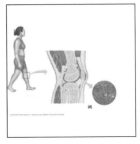

21_05dConnTissue_CNL.jpg

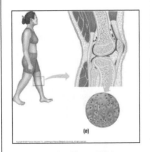

21_05eConnTissue_CL.jpg

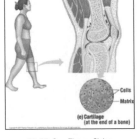

21_05eConnTissue_CNL.jpg

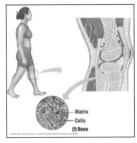

21_05fConnTissue_CL.jpg

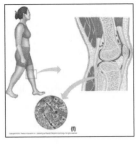

21_05fConnTissue_CNL.jpg

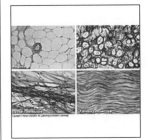

21_05x1ConnectTiss_XLP.jpg

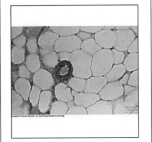

21_05x2Adipose_XUP.jpg

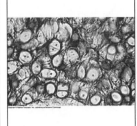

21_05x3Cartilage_XUP.jpg

21_05x4LooseConn_XUP.jpg

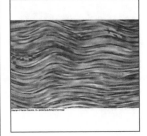

21_05x5FibrConnect_XUP.jpg

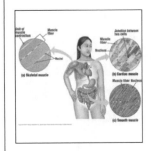

21_06-MuscleTissue_CL.jpg

21_06-MuscleTissue_CNL.jpg

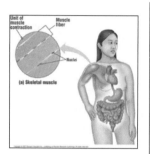

21_06aMuscleTissue_CL.jpg

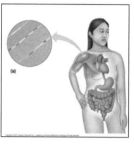

21_06aMuscleTissue_CNL.jpg

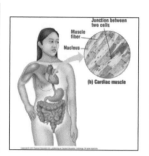

21_06bMuscleTissue_CL.jpg

21_06bMuscleTissue_CNL.jpg

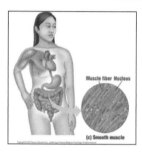

21_06cMuscleTissue_CL.jpg

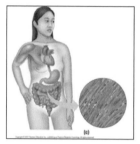

21_06cMuscleTissue_CNL.jpg

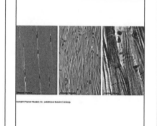

21_06x1aVertebrateMus_XLP.jpg

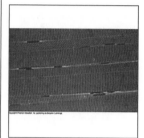

21_06x2SkeletalMus_XUP.jpg

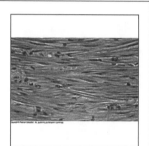

21_06x3SmoothMus_XUP.jpg

21_06x4CardiacMus_XUP.jpg

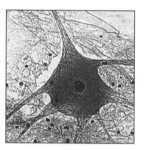

21_06x5Neuron_XUP.jpg

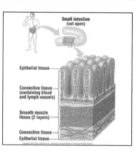

21_07SmallIntest_L.jpg

21_07SmallIntest_U.jpg

21_08a-OrganSystems_L.jpg

21_08a-OrganSystems_U.jpg

21_08a1OrganSystem_L.jpg

21_08a1OrganSystem_U.jpg

21_08a2OrganSystem_L.jpg

21_08a2OrganSystem_U.jpg

21_08a3OrganSystem_L.jpg

21_08a3OrganSystem_U.jpg

21_08b-OrganSystems_L.jpg

21_08b-OrganSystems_U.jpg

21_08b1OrganSystem_L.jpg

21_08b1OrganSystem_U.jpg

21_08b2OrganSystem_L.jpg

21_08b2OrganSystem_U.jpg

21_08b3OrganSystem_L.jpg

21_08b3OrganSystem_U.jpg

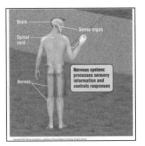

21_08b4OrganSystem_L.jpg

21_08b4OrganSystem_U.jpg

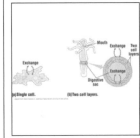

21_09-SimpleOrgEnviron_L.jpg

21_09-SimpleOrgEnviron_U.jpg

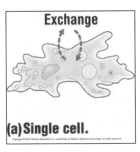

21_09aSimpleOrgEnviron_L.jpg

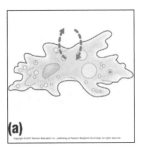

21_09aSimpleOrgEnviron_U.jpg

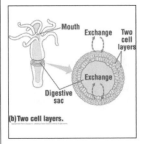

21_09bSimpleOrgEnviron_L.jpg

21_09bSimpleOrgEnviron_U.jpg

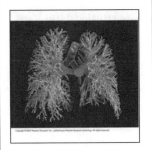

21_10Lungs_UP.jpg

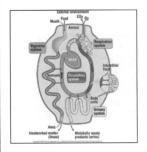

21_11IndirectExchange_L.jpg

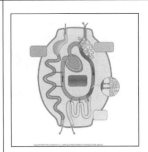

21_11IndirectExchange_U.jpg

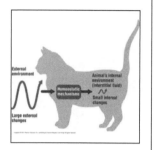

21_12Homeostasis_L.jpg

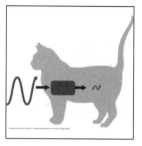

21_12Homeostasis_U.jpg

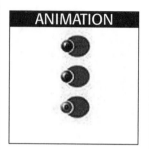

21_13NegativeFeedback_A.swf

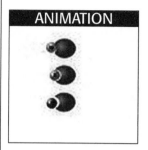

21_13PositiveFeedback_A.swf

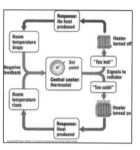

21_13NegativeFeedback_L.jpg

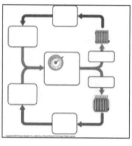

21_13NegativeFeedback_U.jpg

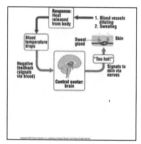

21_14Thermoregulation1_L.jpg

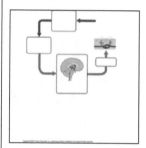

21_14Thermoregulation1_U.jpg

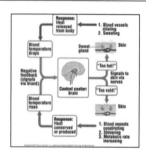

21_14Thermoregulation2_L.jpg

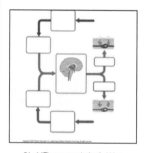

21_14Thermoregulation2_U.jpg

21_15-ThermoregMethods_LP.jpg

21_15-ThermoregMethods_UP.jpg

21_15aThermoregMethods_LP.jpg

21_15aThermoregMethods_UP.jpg

21_15bThermoregMethods_LP.jpg

21_15bThermoregMethods_UP.jpg

21_15x1FoxInSnow_XUP.jpg

21_15x2HarborSeal_XUP.jpg

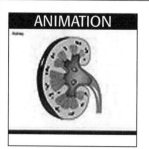

21_16NephronIntroduction_A.swf

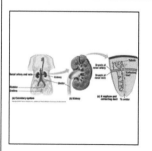

21_16-UrinarySystem_L.jpg

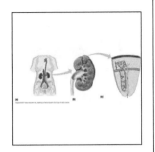

21_16-UrinarySystem_U.jpg

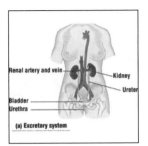

21_16aUrinarySystem_L.jpg

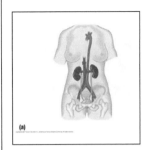

21_16aUrinarySystem_U.jpg

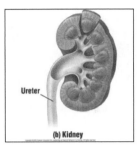

21_16bUrinarySystem_L.jpg

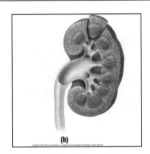

21_16bUrinarySystem_U.jpg

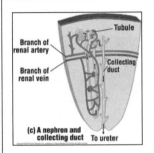

21_16cUrinarySystem_L.jpg

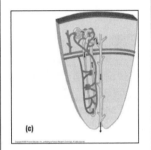

21_16cUrinarySystem_U.jpg

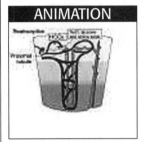

21_17aBowmansCapsule_A.swf

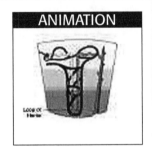

21_17bLoopOfHenle_A.swf

21_17cCollectingDuct_A.swf

21_17dEffectOfADH_A.swf

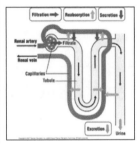

21_17UrinarySystemFxn_L.jpg

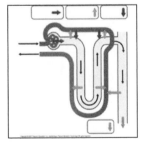

21_17UrinarySystemFxn_U.jpg

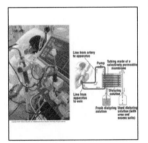

21_18Dialysis_CL.jpg

21_18Dialysis_CNL.jpg

21_19-ConvergentEvo_LP.jpg

21_19-ConvergentEvo_UP.jpg

21_19aConvergentEvo_LP.jpg

21_19aConvergentEvo_UP.jpg

21_19bConvergentEvo_LP.jpg

21_19bConvergentEvo_UP.jpg

(c) Shark

21_19cConvergentEvo_LP.jpg

(c)

21_19cConvergentEvo_UP.jpg

(d) Tuna

21_19dConvergentEvo_LP.jpg

(d)

21_19dConvergentEvo_UP.jpg

(e) Penguins

21_19eConvergentEvo_LP.jpg

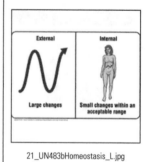

(e)

21_19eConvergentEvo_UP.jpg

(f) Submarine

21_19fConvergentEvo_LP.jpg

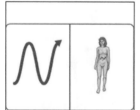

(f)

21_19fConvergentEvo_UP.jpg

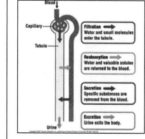

21_UN483aAnimalOrg_L.jpg

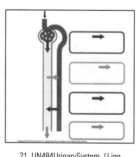

21_UN483aAnimalOrg_U.jpg

21_UN483bHomeostasis_L.jpg

21_UN483bHomeostasis_U.jpg

21_UN484UrinarySystem_L.jpg

21_UN484UrinarySystem_U.jpg

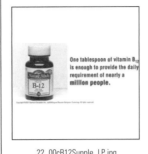

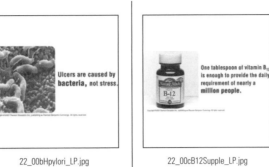

22_00aIntestine_LP.jpg

22_00bHpylori_LP.jpg

22_00cB12Supple_LP.jpg

22_00dSaliva_LP.jpg

22_01deRossi_UP.jpg

22_02-AnimalDiets_LP.jpg

22_02-AnimalDiets_UP.jpg

22_02aAnimalDiets_LP.jpg

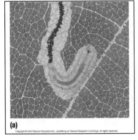

22_02aAnimalDiets_UP.jpg

22_02bAnimalDiets_LP.jpg

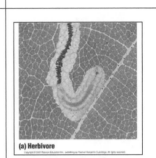

22_02bAnimalDiets_UP.jpg

22_02cAnimalDiets_LP.jpg

22_02cAnimalDiets_UP.jpg

22_02LobsterMouthParts_SV.mpg

22_02LobsterMouthParts_VT.swf

22_02SharkEatSeal_SV.mpg

22_02SharkEatSeal_VT.swf

22_02xAnimEatingCol_XUP.jpg

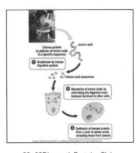

22_03DismantleProtein_CL.jpg

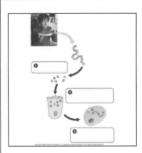

22_03DismantleProtein_CNL.jpg

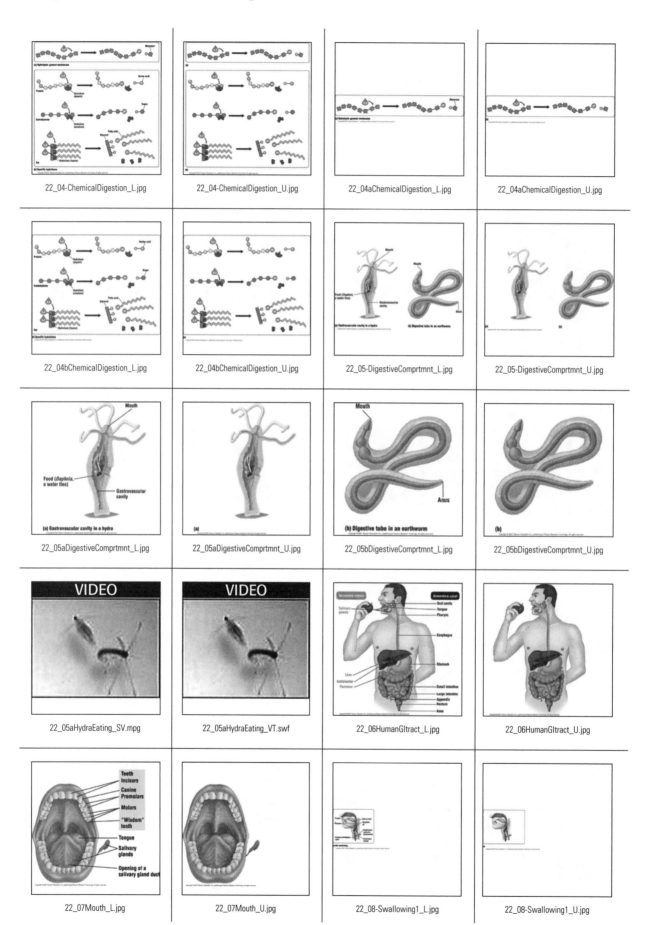

22_04-ChemicalDigestion_L.jpg

22_04-ChemicalDigestion_U.jpg

22_04aChemicalDigestion_L.jpg

22_04aChemicalDigestion_U.jpg

22_04bChemicalDigestion_L.jpg

22_04bChemicalDigestion_U.jpg

22_05-DigestiveComprtmnt_L.jpg

22_05-DigestiveComprtmnt_U.jpg

22_05aDigestiveComprtmnt_L.jpg

22_05aDigestiveComprtmnt_U.jpg

22_05bDigestiveComprtmnt_L.jpg

22_05bDigestiveComprtmnt_U.jpg

22_05aHydraEating_SV.mpg

22_05aHydraEating_VT.swf

22_06HumanGItract_L.jpg

22_06HumanGItract_U.jpg

22_07Mouth_L.jpg

22_07Mouth_U.jpg

22_08-Swallowing1_L.jpg

22_08-Swallowing1_U.jpg

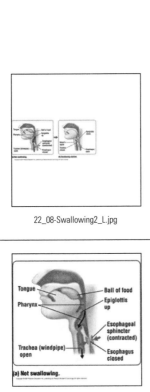

22_08-Swallowing2_L.jpg

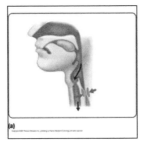

22_08-Swallowing2_U.jpg

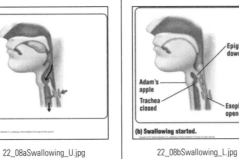

22_08-Swallowing3_L.jpg

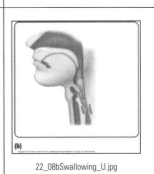

22_08-Swallowing3_U.jpg

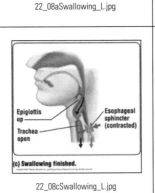

22_08aSwallowing_L.jpg

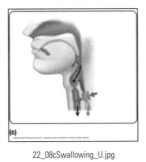

22_08aSwallowing_U.jpg

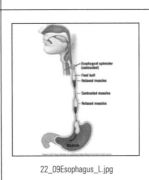

22_08bSwallowing_L.jpg

22_08bSwallowing_U.jpg

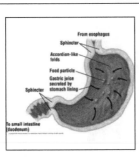

22_08cSwallowing_L.jpg

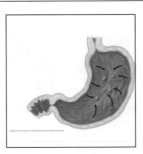

22_08cSwallowing_U.jpg

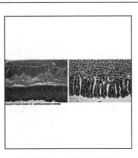

22_09Esophagus_L.jpg

22_09Esophagus_U.jpg

22_10Stomach_L.jpg

22_10Stomach_U.jpg

22_10x1StomachLining_XUP.jpg

22_10x2StomachLining_XUP.jpg

22_10x3StomachLining_XUP.jpg

22_11WilliamBeaumont_UP.jpg

22_12Hpylori_LP.jpg

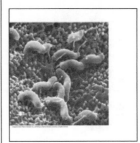

22_12Hpylori_UP.jpg

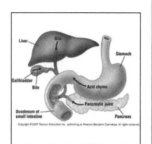

22_13Duodenum_L.jpg

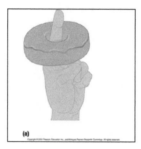

22_13Duodenum_U.jpg

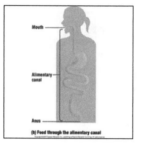

22_14-DonutAnalogy_L.jpg

22_14-DonutAnalogy_U.jpg

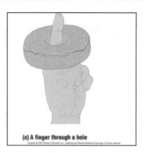

22_14aDonutAnalogy_L.jpg

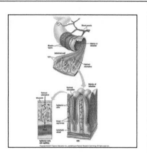

22_14aDonutAnalogy_U.jpg

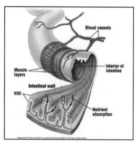

22_14bDonutAnalogy_L.jpg

22_14bDonutAnalogy_U.jpg

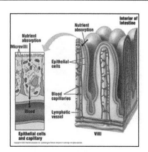

22_15-SmallIntest_L.jpg

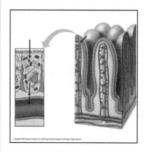

22_15-SmallIntest_U.jpg

22_15aSmallIntest_L.jpg

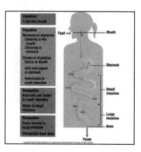

22_15aSmallIntest_U.jpg

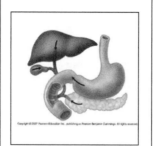

22_15bSmallIntest_L.jpg

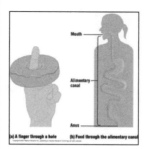

22_15bSmallIntest_U.jpg

22_15xLargeIntestine_XUP.jpg

22_16FoodProcess_L.jpg

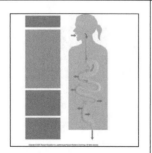

22_16FoodProcess_U.jpg

22_17FoodPyramid_L.jpg

22_17FoodPyramid_U.jpg

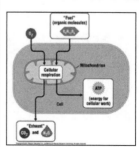

22_18CellRespiration_L.jpg

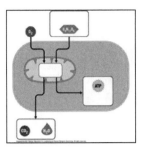

22_18CellRespiration_U.jpg

22_19-EssentAminoAcids_CL.jpg

22_19-EssentAminoAcids_CNL.jpg

22_19aEssentAminoAcids_CL.jpg

22_19aEssentAminoAcids_CNL.jpg

22_19bEssentAminoAcids_UP.jpg

22_20NutritionLabel_L.jpg

22_21Kwashiorkor_UP.jpg

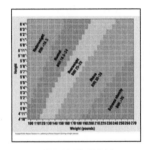

22_22HealthyWgtBMI_L.jpg

22_23HungryMouse_UP.jpg

22_24HunterGatherer_UP.jpg

22_T01ExerciseKcal_T.jpg

22_T02Vitamins_T.jpg

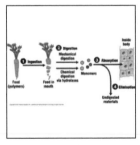

22_UN502aFoodProcess_L.jpg

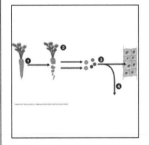

22_UN502aFoodProcess_U.jpg

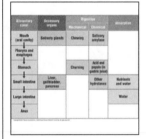

22_UN502bDigestSysMap_L.jpg

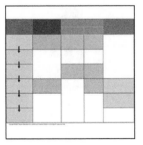

22_UN502bDigestSysMap_U.jpg

22_UN503NutritionLabel_L.jpg

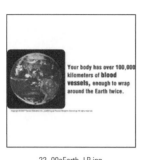

23_00aEarth_LP.jpg

23_00bRedBloodCells_LP.jpg

23_00cCigarette_LP.jpg

23_00dLungs_LP.jpg

23_01TourOfShame_UP.jpg

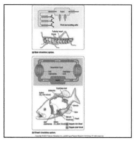

23_02-OpenClosedCirc_L.jpg

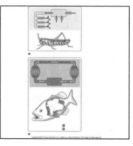

23_02-OpenClosedCirc_U.jpg

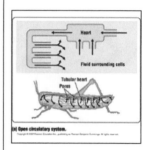

23_02aOpenClosedCirc_L.jpg

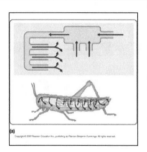

23_02aOpenClosedCirc_U.jpg

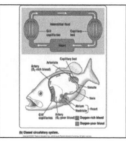

23_02bOpenClosedCirc_L.jpg

23_02bOpenClosedCirc_U.jpg

23_03-DoubleCircSystem_L.jpg

23_03-DoubleCircSystem_U.jpg

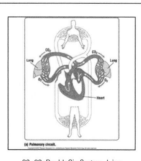

23_03aDoubleCircSystem_L.jpg

23_03aDoubleCircSystem_U.jpg

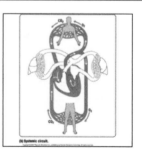

23_03bDoubleCircSystem_L.jpg

23_03bDoubleCircSystem_U.jpg

23_04PathOfBloodFlow_A.swf

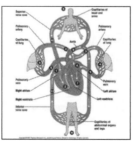

23_04HumanCardioSys_L.jpg

23_04HumanCardioSys_U.jpg

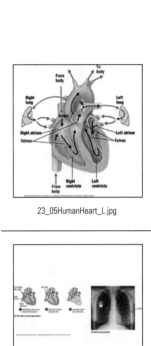

23_05HumanHeart_L.jpg

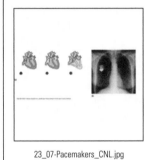

23_05HumanHeart_U.jpg

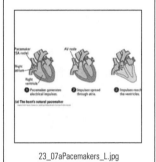

23_06CardiacCycle_L.jpg

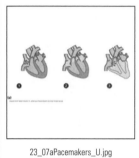

23_06CardiacCycle_U.jpg

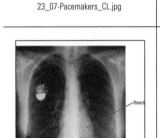

23_07-Pacemakers_CL.jpg

23_07-Pacemakers_CNL.jpg

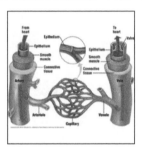

23_07aPacemakers_L.jpg

23_07aPacemakers_U.jpg

23_07bPacemakers_LP.jpg

23_07bPacemakers_UP.jpg

23_08Bloodvessels_L.jpg

23_08Bloodvessels_U.jpg

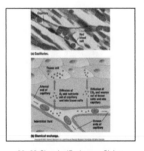

23_09-ChemicalExchange_CL.jpg

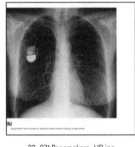

23_09-ChemicalExchange_CNL.jpg

23_09aChemicalExchange_LP.jpg

23_09aChemicalExchange_UP.jpg

23_09bChemicalExchange_L.jpg

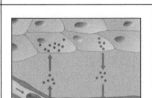

23_09bChemicalExchange_U.jpg

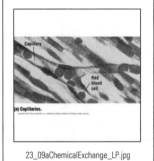

23_10VenousFlow_L.jpg

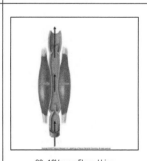

23_10VenousFlow_U.jpg

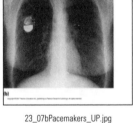
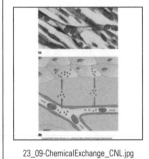

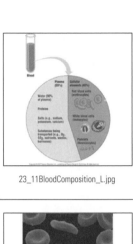

23_11BloodComposition_L.jpg

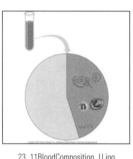

23_11BloodComposition_U.jpg

23_12-CellComponents_LP.jpg

23_12-CellComponents_UP.jpg

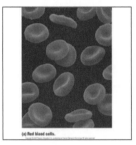

23_12aCellComponents_LP.jpg

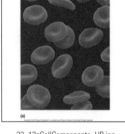

23_12aCellComponents_UP.jpg

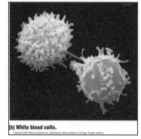

23_12bCellComponents_LP.jpg

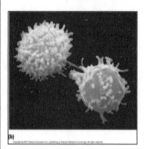

23_12bCellComponents_UP.jpg

23_12cCellComponents_LP.jpg

23_12cCellComponents_UP.jpg

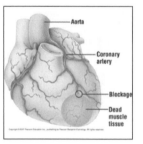

23_13HeartAttack_L.jpg

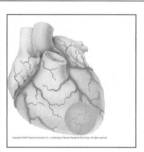

23_13HeartAttack_U.jpg

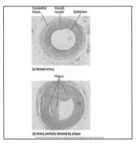

23_14-Atherosclerosis_LP.jpg

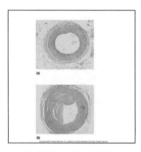

23_14-Atherosclerosis_UP.jpg

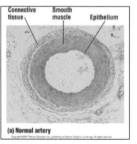

23_14aAtherosclerosis_LP.jpg

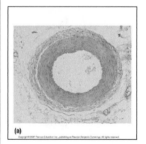

23_14aAtherosclerosis_UP.jpg

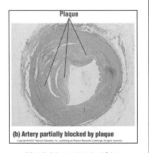

23_14bAtherosclerosis_LP.jpg

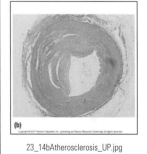

23_14bAtherosclerosis_UP.jpg

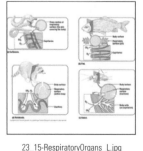

23_15-RespiratoryOrgans_L.jpg

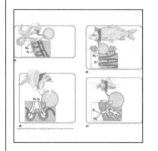

23_15-RespiratoryOrgans_U.jpg

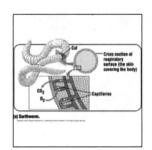

23_15aRespiratoryOrgans_L.jpg

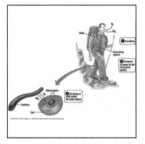

23_15aRespiratoryOrgans_U.jpg

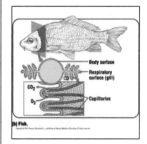

23_15bRespiratoryOrgans_L.jpg

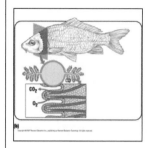

23_15bRespiratoryOrgans_U.jpg

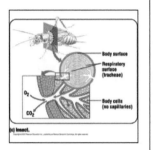

23_15cRespiratoryOrgans_L.jpg

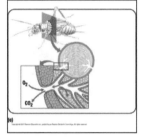

23_15cRespiratoryOrgans_U.jpg

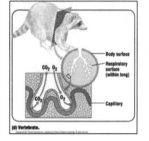

23_15dRespiratoryOrgans_L.jpg

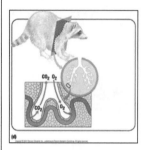

23_15dRespiratoryOrgans_U.jpg

23_16GasExchPhases_L.jpg

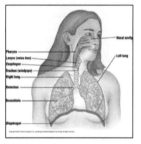

23_16GasExchPhases_U.jpg

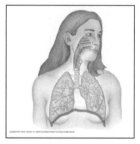

23_17HumanRespSyst_L.jpg

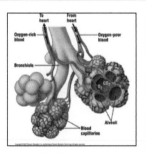

23_17HumanRespSyst_U.jpg

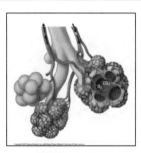

23_18Alveoli_L.jpg

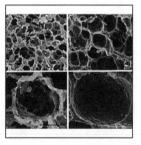

23_18Alveoli_U.jpg

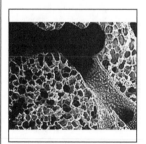

23_18x1AlveoliSEMs_XUP.jpg

23_18x2AlveoliSEM_XUP.jpg

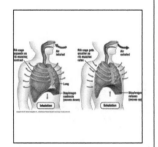

23_19InhaleExhale_L.jpg

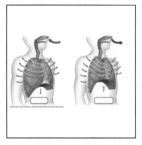

23_19InhaleExhale_U.jpg

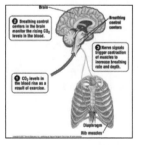

23_20BreathControlCtr_L.jpg

23_20BreathControlCtr_U.jpg

23_21GasTransport_L.jpg

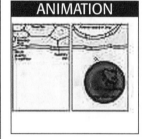

23_21GasTransport_U.jpg

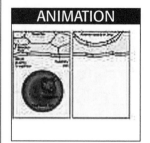

23_22aO2FromBlootoTissue_A.swf

23_22bCO2FromTissutoBloo_A.swf

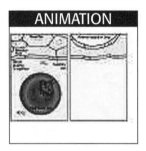

23_22cCO2FromBloodtoLung_A.swf

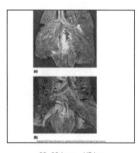

23_22dO2FromLungstoBlood_A.swf

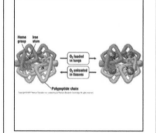

23_22Hemoglobin_L.jpg

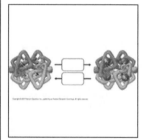

23_22Hemoglobin_U.jpg

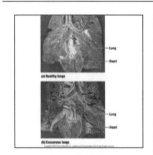

23_23-Lungs_LP.jpg

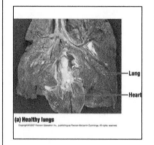

23_23-Lungs_UP.jpg

23_23aLungs_LP.jpg

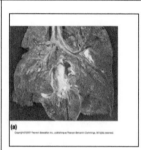

23_23aLungs_UP.jpg

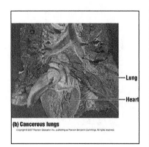

23_23bLungs_LP.jpg

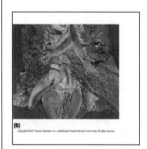

23_23bLungs_UP.jpg

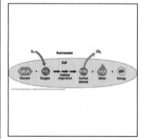

23_24Lungfish_UP.jpg

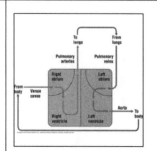

23_UN517CellResp_L.jpg

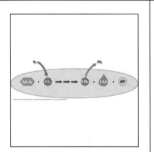

23_UN517CellResp_U.jpg

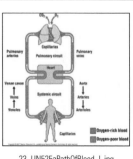

23_UN525aPathOfBlood_L.jpg

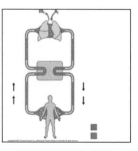

23_UN525aPathOfBlood_U.jpg

23_UN525bHowHeartWorks_L.jpg

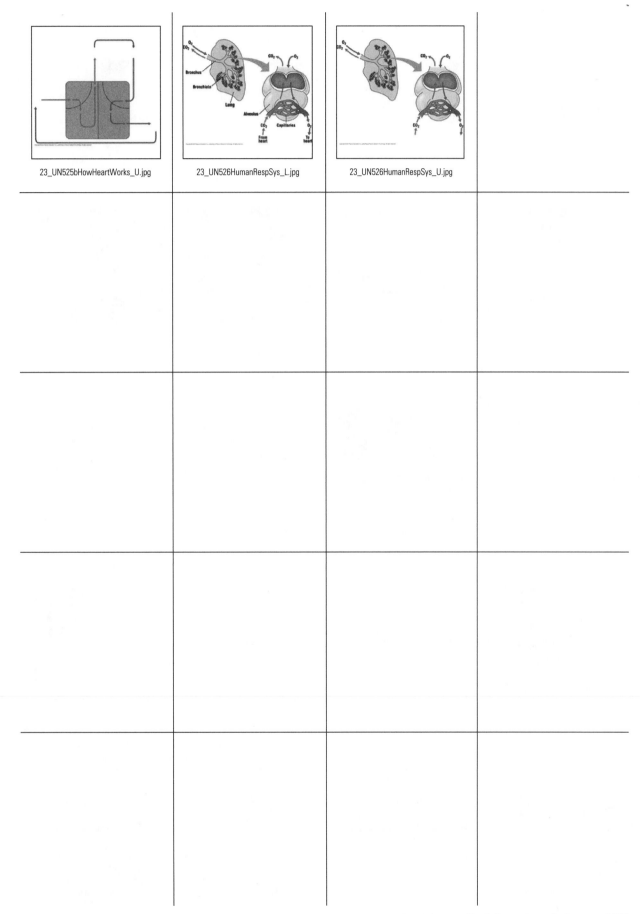

23_UN525bHowHeartWorks_U.jpg

23_UN526HumanRespSys_L.jpg

23_UN526HumanRespSys_U.jpg

Chapter 24 The Body's Defenses

24_00aBacteria_LP.jpg

24_00bVaccination_LP.jpg

24_00cHealthySkin_LP.jpg

24_00dAIDS_LP.jpg

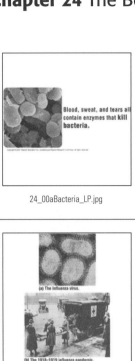

24_01-FluPandemic_LP.jpg

24_01-FluPandemic_UP.jpg

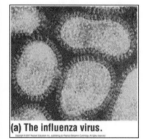

24_01aFluPandemic_LP.jpg

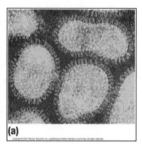

24_01aFluPandemic_UP.jpg

24_01bFluPandemic_LP.jpg

24_01bFluPandemic_UP.jpg

24_02DefensesOverview_L.jpg

24_02DefensesOverview_U.jpg

24_03Cilia_UP.jpg

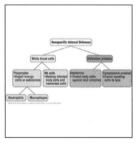

24_04NonspecificDefense_L.jpg

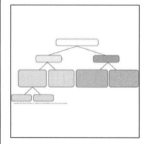

24_04NonspecificDefense_U.jpg

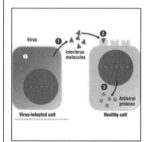

24_05Interferon_L.jpg

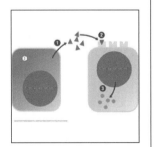

24_05Interferon_U.jpg

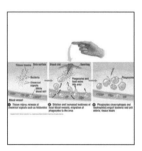

24_06InflammatoryResp_CL.jpg

24_06InflammatoryResp_CNL.jpg

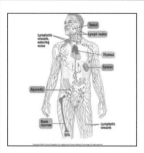

24_07LymphaticSyst_L.jpg

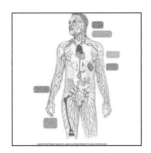

24_07LymphaticSyst_U.jpg

24_08Vaccination_UP.jpg

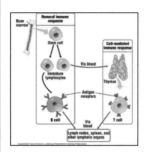

24_09LymphocyteDev_L.jpg

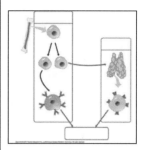

24_09LymphocyteDev_U.jpg

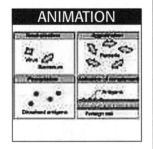

24_10Antibodies_A.swf

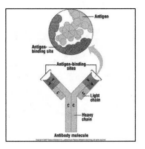

24_10Antibody_L.jpg

24_10Antibody_U.jpg

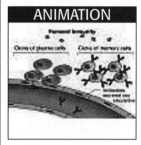

24_11RoleOfBCells_A.swf

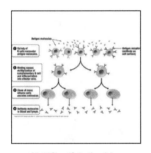

24_11ClonalSelection_L.jpg

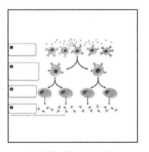

24_11ClonalSelection_U.jpg

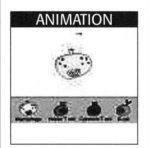

24_12HelperTCells_A.swf

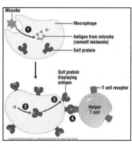

24_12HelperTMacrophage_L.jpg

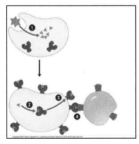

24_12HelperTMacrophage_U.jpg

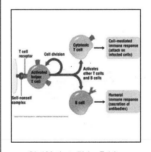

24_13ActivatedHelperT_L.jpg

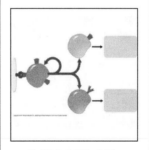

24_13ActivatedHelperT_U.jpg

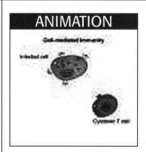

24_14CytotoxicTCells_A.swf

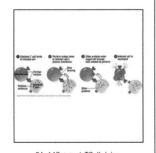

24_14CytotoxicTCell_L.jpg

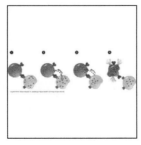

24_14CytotoxicTCell_U.jpg

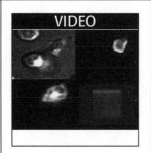

24_14TCellReceptors_SV.mpg

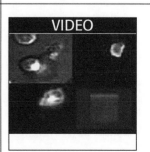

24_14TCellReceptors_VT.swf

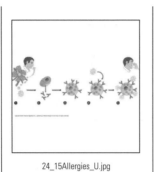

24_15Allergies_L.jpg

24_15Allergies_U.jpg

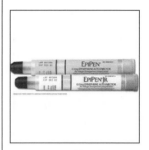

24_15xAllergySpores_XUP.jpg

24_16Epinephrine_UP.jpg

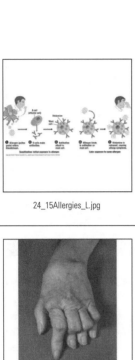

24_17RheumatoidArth_UP.jpg

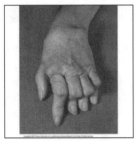
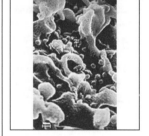

24_17xArthritisXray_XUP.jpg

24_18AIDSeducation_UP.jpg

24_18x1HIVonLymp_XLP.jpg

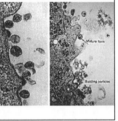
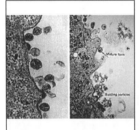

24_18x2_HIVBudding_XLP.jpg

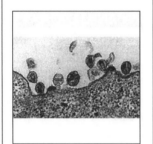

24_18x2aHIVBudding_XUP.jpg

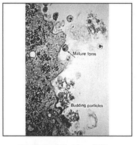

24_18x2bHIVBudding_XLP.jpg

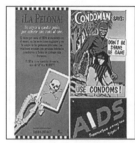

24_18x3AIDSPosters_XUP.jpg

24_19HIVReproCycle_A.swf

24_19HIVattack_UP.jpg

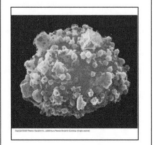
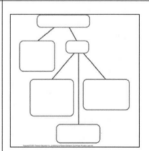

24_UN542aNonspecDef_L.jpg

24_UN542aNonspecDef_U.jpg

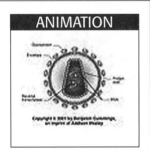
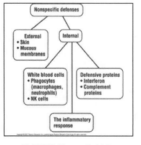

24_UN542bLymphocytes_L.jpg

24_UN542bLymphocytes_U.jpg

24_UN542cClonalSelection_L.jpg

24_UN542cClonalSelection_U.jpg

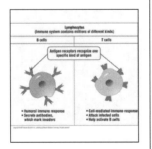
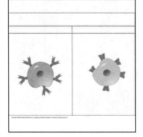
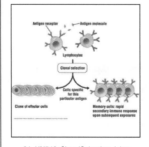
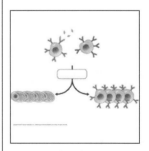

Chapter 25 Hormones

25_00aHormones_LP.jpg

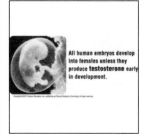

25_00bHumanEmbryo_LP.jpg

25_00cStress_LP.jpg

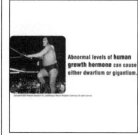

25_00dGigantism_LP.jpg

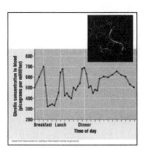

25_01HungerHormone_L.jpg

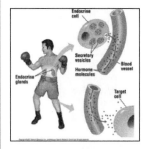

25_02HormoneSecretion_L.jpg

25_02HormoneSecretion_U.jpg

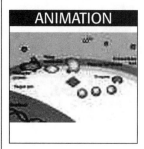

25_03WaterSolubleHormon_A.swf

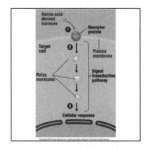

25_03AminoAcidHormone_L.jpg

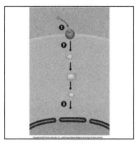

25_03AminoAcidHormone_U.jpg

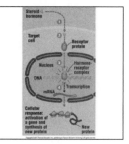

25_04LipidSolubleHormon_A.swf

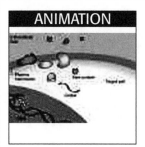

25_04SteroidHormone_L.jpg

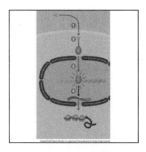

25_04SteroidHormone_U.jpg

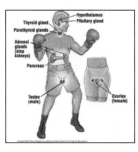

25_05EndocrineGlands_L.jpg

25_05EndocrineGlands_U.jpg

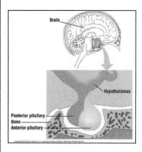

25_06Pituitary_L.jpg

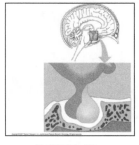

25_06Pituitary_U.jpg

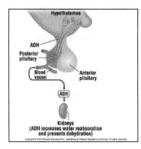

25_07ADH_L.jpg

25_07ADH_U.jpg

25_08-GrowthHormDisorder_LP.jpg

25_08-GrowthHormDisorder_UP.jpg

(a) Overproduction of GH during development.

25_08aGrowthHormDisorder_LP.jpg

(a)

25_08aGrowthHormDisorder_UP.jpg

(b) Overproduction of GH during adulthood.

25_08bGrowthHormDisorder_LP.jpg

(b)

25_08bGrowthHormDisorder_UP.jpg

(c) Underproduction of GH during development.

25_08cGrowthHormDisorder_LP.jpg

(c)

25_08cGrowthHormDisorder_UP.jpg

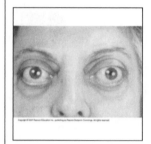

25_09GravesDisease_UP.jpg

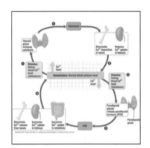

25_10CalciumHomeostasis_L.jpg

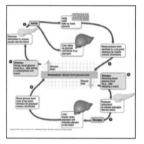

25_10CalciumHomeostasis_U.jpg

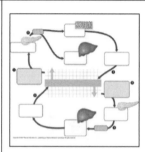

25_11GlucoseHomeostasis_L.jpg

25_11GlucoseHomeostasis_U.jpg

25_12StressResponse1_L.jpg

25_12StressResponse1_U.jpg

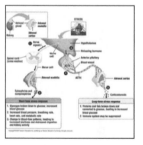

25_12StressResponse2_L.jpg

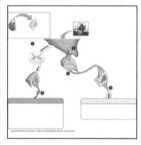

25_12StressResponse2_U.jpg

25_13Prolactin_UP.jpg

25_T01aEndocrineGlands_T.jpg

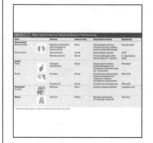

25_T01bEndocrineGlands_T.jpg

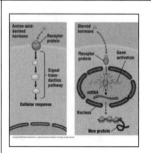

25_UN557aHormones_L.jpg

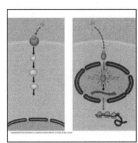

25_UN557aHormones_U.jpg

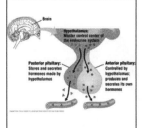

25_UN557bHypothalPituit_L.jpg

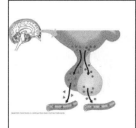

25_UN557bHypothalPituit_U.jpg

26_00aOriginalCell_LP.jpg

26_00bSpermEgg_LP.jpg

26_00cOvulation_LP.jpg

26_00dElephants_LP.jpg

26_01Septuplets_UP.jpg

26_02-AsexualReproduct_LP.jpg

26_02-AsexualReproduct_UP.jpg

26_02aAsexualReproduct_LP.jpg

26_02aAsexualReproduct_UP.jpg

26_02bAsexualReproduct_LP.jpg

26_02bAsexualReproduct_UP.jpg

26_03-ReproSchemes_LP.jpg

26_03-ReproSchemes_UP.jpg

26_03aReproSchemes_LP.jpg

26_03aReproSchemes_UP.jpg

26_03bReproSchemes_LP.jpg

26_03bReproSchemes_UP.jpg

26_03cReproSchemes_LP.jpg

26_03cReproSchemes_UP.jpg

26_03aRotifer_SV.mpg

26_03aRotifer_VT.swf

26_04FemaleReproAnatomy_A.swf

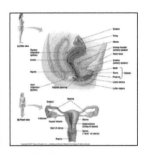

26_04-FemaleRepro_L.jpg

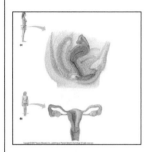

26_04-FemaleRepro_U.jpg

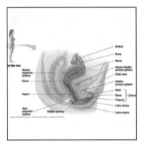

26_04aFemaleRepro_L.jpg

26_04aFemaleRepro_U.jpg

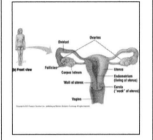

26_04bFemaleRepro_L.jpg

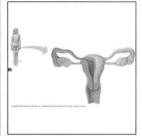

26_04bFemaleRepro_U.jpg

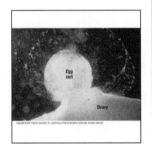

26_05Ovulation_LP.jpg

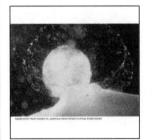

26_05Ovulation_UP.jpg

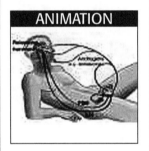

26_06MaleHormones_A.swf

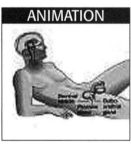

26_06MaleReproAnatomy_A.swf

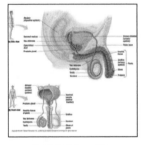

26_06_MaleRepro_L.jpg

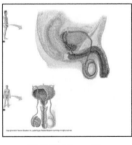

26_06_MaleRepro_U.jpg

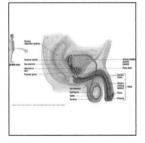

26_06aMaleRepro_L.jpg

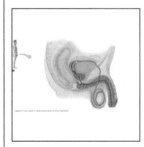

26_06aMaleRepro_U.jpg

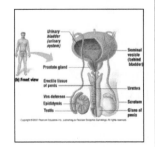

26_06bMaleRepro_L.jpg

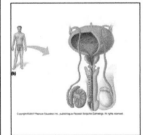

26_06bMaleRepro_U.jpg

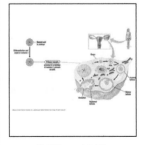

26_07Oogenesis1_L.jpg

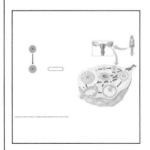

26_07Oogenesis1_U.jpg

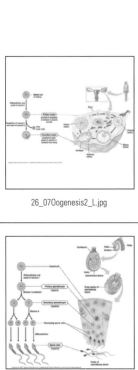

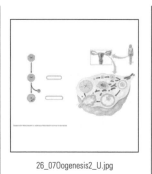

26_07Oogenesis2_L.jpg

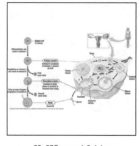

26_07Oogenesis2_U.jpg

26_07Oogenesis3_L.jpg

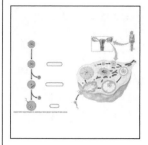

26_07Oogenesis3_U.jpg

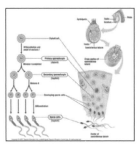

26_08Spermatogenesis_L.jpg

26_08Spermatogenesis_U.jpg

VIDEO

26_08HydraSperm_SV.mpg

VIDEO

26_08HydraSperm_VT.swf

ANIMATION

26_09Ovulation_A.swf

ANIMATION

26_09PostOvulation_A.swf

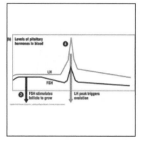

26_09-FemaleReproCycle_L.jpg

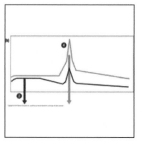

26_09-FemaleReproCycle_U.jpg

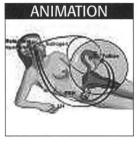

26_09aFemaleReproCycle_L.jpg

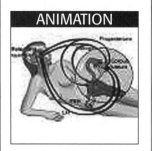

26_09aFemaleReproCycle_U.jpg

26_09bFemaleReproCycle_L.jpg

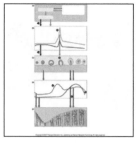

26_09bFemaleReproCycle_U.jpg

26_09cFemaleReproCycle_L.jpg

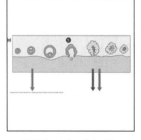

26_09cFemaleReproCycle_U.jpg

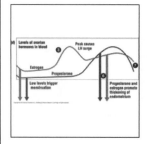

26_09dFemaleReproCycle_L.jpg

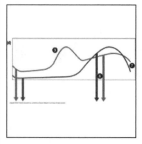

26_09dFemaleReproCycle_U.jpg

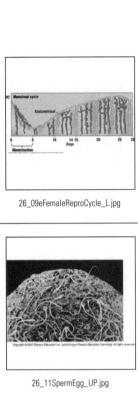

26_09eFemaleReproCycle_L.jpg

26_09eFemaleReproCycle_U.jpg

26_10Contraceptives_LP.jpg

26_10Contraceptives_UP.jpg

26_11SpermEgg_UP.jpg

26_12Sperm_L.jpg

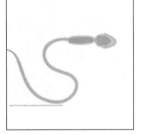

26_12Sperm_U.jpg

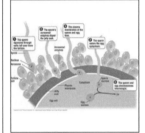

26_13Fertilization_L.jpg

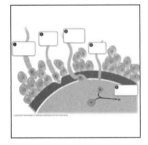

26_13Fertilization_U.jpg

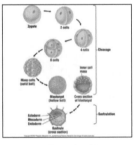

26_14EmbryoDev_L.jpg

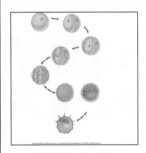

26_14EmbryoDev_U.jpg

26_14SeaUrchinTimeLapse_SV.mpg

26_14SeaUrchinTimeLapse_VT.swf

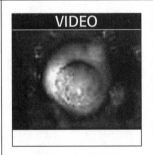

26_14XenopusDevelop_SV.mpg

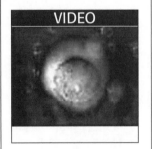

26_14XenopusDevelop_VT.swf

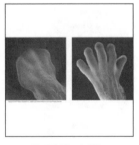

26_15-CellDeath_UP.jpg

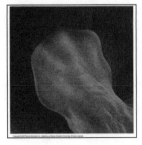

26_15aCellDeath_UP.jpg

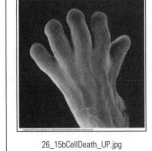

26_15bCellDeath_UP.jpg

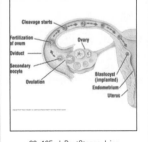

26_16EarlyDevtStages_L.jpg

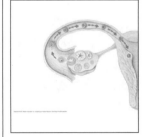

26_16EarlyDevtStages_U.jpg

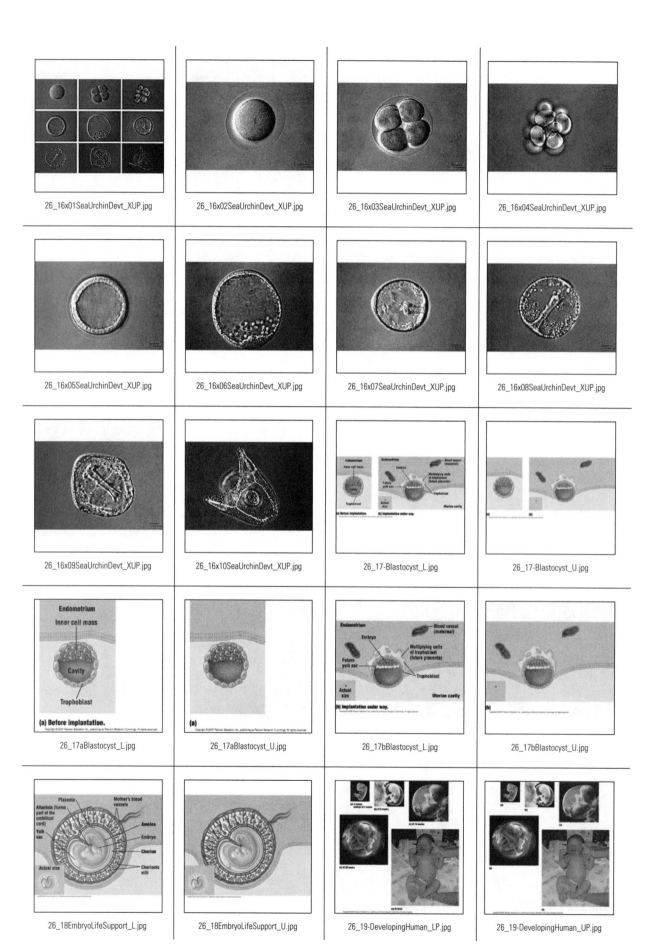

26_16x01SeaUrchinDevt_XUP.jpg

26_16x02SeaUrchinDevt_XUP.jpg

26_16x03SeaUrchinDevt_XUP.jpg

26_16x04SeaUrchinDevt_XUP.jpg

26_16x05SeaUrchinDevt_XUP.jpg

26_16x06SeaUrchinDevt_XUP.jpg

26_16x07SeaUrchinDevt_XUP.jpg

26_16x08SeaUrchinDevt_XUP.jpg

26_16x09SeaUrchinDevt_XUP.jpg

26_16x10SeaUrchinDevt_XUP.jpg

26_17-Blastocyst_L.jpg

26_17-Blastocyst_U.jpg

26_17aBlastocyst_L.jpg

26_17aBlastocyst_U.jpg

26_17bBlastocyst_L.jpg

26_17bBlastocyst_U.jpg

26_18EmbryoLifeSupport_L.jpg

26_18EmbryoLifeSupport_U.jpg

26_19-DevelopingHuman_LP.jpg

26_19-DevelopingHuman_UP.jpg

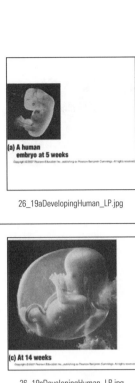

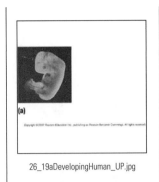

(a) A human
embryo at 5 weeks

26_19aDevelopingHuman_LP.jpg

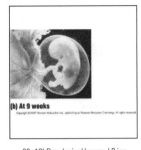

(a)

26_19aDevelopingHuman_UP.jpg

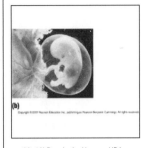

(b) At 9 weeks

26_19bDevelopingHuman_LP.jpg

(b)

26_19bDevelopingHuman_UP.jpg

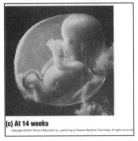

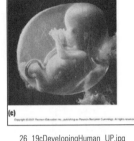

(c) At 14 weeks

26_19cDevelopingHuman_LP.jpg

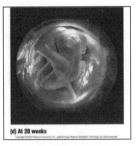

(c)

26_19cDevelopingHuman_UP.jpg

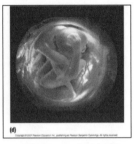

(d) At 20 weeks

26_19dDevelopingHuman_LP.jpg

(d)

26_19dDevelopingHuman_UP.jpg

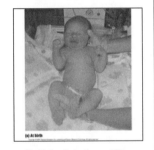

(e) At birth

26_19eDevelopingHuman_LP.jpg

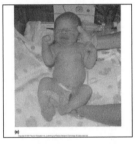

(e)

26_19eDevelopingHuman_UP.jpg

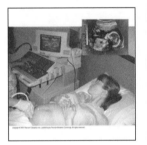

26_20Ultrasound_UP.jpg

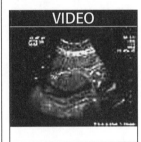

VIDEO

26_20UltrasoundOfFetus2_SV.mpg

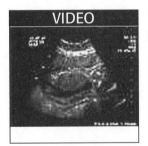

VIDEO

26_20UltrasoundOfFetus2_VT.swf

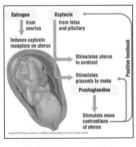

26_21LaborHormones_L.jpg

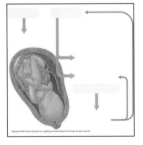

26_21LaborHormones_U.jpg

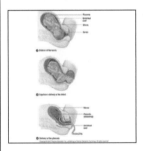

26_22-LaborStages_L.jpg

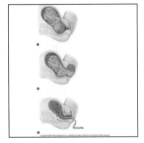

26_22-LaborStages_U.jpg

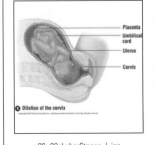

1 Dilation of the cervix

26_22aLaborStages_L.jpg

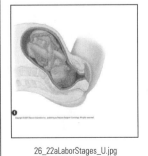

26_22aLaborStages_U.jpg

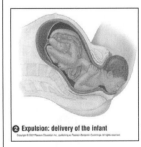

2 Expulsion: delivery of the infant

26_22bLaborStages_L.jpg

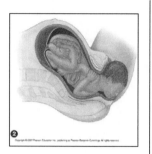

26_22bLaborStages_U.jpg

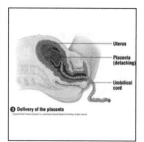

26_22cLaborStages_L.jpg

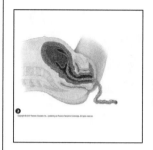

26_22cLaborStages_U.jpg

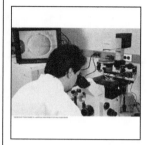

26_23InVitroFertilizat_UP.jpg

26_T01Contraception_T.jpg

26_T02STDs_T.jpg

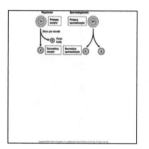

26_UN582aGametogenesis1_L.jpg

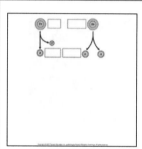

26_UN582aGametogenesis1_U.jpg

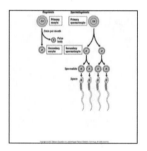

26_UN582aGametogenesis2_L.jpg

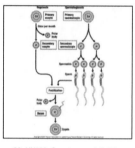

26_UN582aGametogenesis2_U.jpg

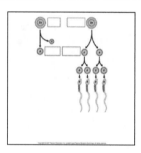

26_UN582aGametogenesis3_L.jpg

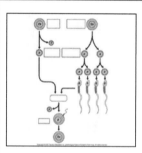

26_UN582aGametogenesis3_U.jpg

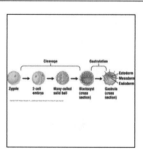

26_UN582bEmbryonicDevt_L.jpg

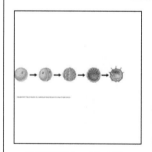

26_UN582bEmbryonicDevt_U.jpg

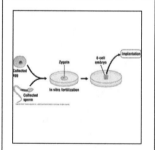

26_UN583InVitroFertiliz_L.jpg

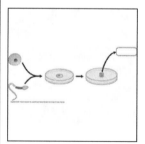

26_UN583InVitroFertiliz_U.jpg

Chapter 27 Nervous, Sensory, and Motor Systems

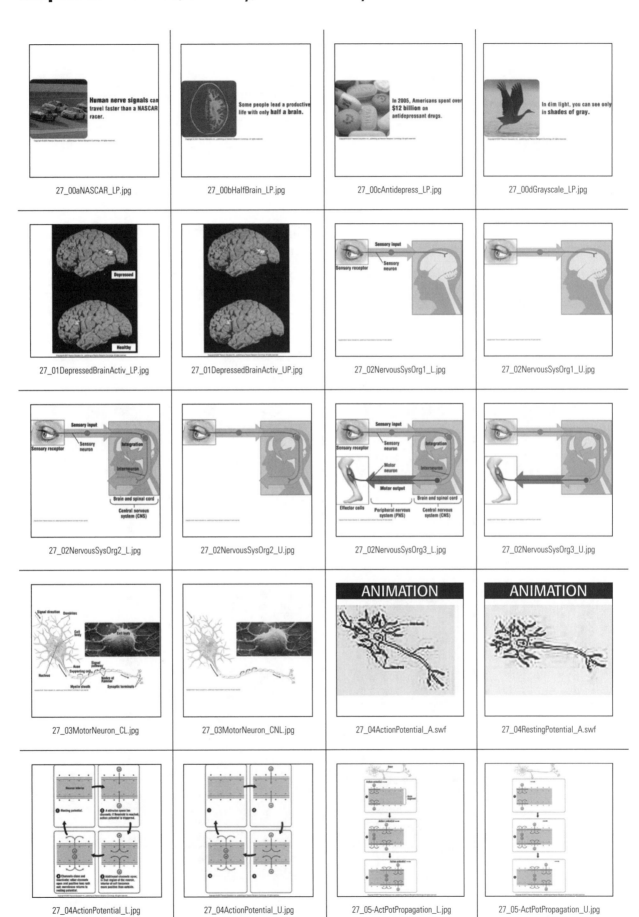

27_00aNASCAR_LP.jpg

27_00bHalfBrain_LP.jpg

27_00cAntidepress_LP.jpg

27_00dGrayscale_LP.jpg

27_01DepressedBrainActiv_LP.jpg

27_01DepressedBrainActiv_UP.jpg

27_02NervousSysOrg1_L.jpg

27_02NervousSysOrg1_U.jpg

27_02NervousSysOrg2_L.jpg

27_02NervousSysOrg2_U.jpg

27_02NervousSysOrg3_L.jpg

27_02NervousSysOrg3_U.jpg

27_03MotorNeuron_CL.jpg

27_03MotorNeuron_CNL.jpg

27_04ActionPotential_A.swf

27_04RestingPotential_A.swf

27_04ActionPotential_L.jpg

27_04ActionPotential_U.jpg

27_05-ActPotPropagation_L.jpg

27_05-ActPotPropagation_U.jpg

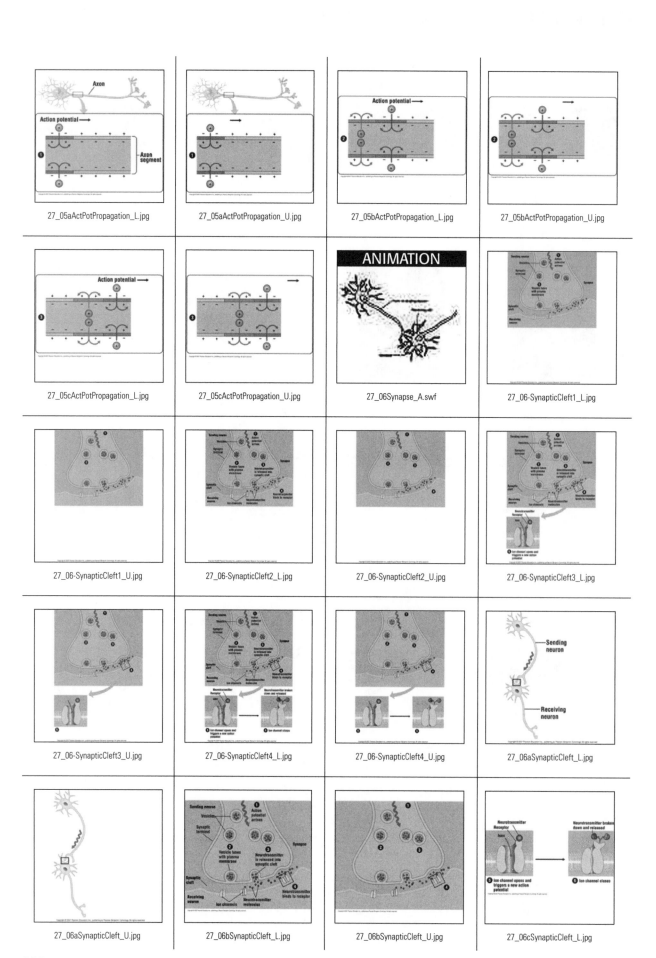

27_05aActPotPropagation_L.jpg

27_05aActPotPropagation_U.jpg

27_05bActPotPropagation_L.jpg

27_05bActPotPropagation_U.jpg

27_05cActPotPropagation_L.jpg

27_05cActPotPropagation_U.jpg

27_06Synapse_A.swf

27_06-SynapticCleft1_L.jpg

27_06-SynapticCleft1_U.jpg

27_06-SynapticCleft2_L.jpg

27_06-SynapticCleft2_U.jpg

27_06-SynapticCleft3_L.jpg

27_06-SynapticCleft3_U.jpg

27_06-SynapticCleft4_L.jpg

27_06-SynapticCleft4_U.jpg

27_06aSynapticCleft_L.jpg

27_06aSynapticCleft_U.jpg

27_06bSynapticCleft_L.jpg

27_06bSynapticCleft_U.jpg

27_06cSynapticCleft_L.jpg

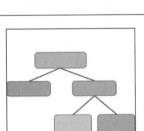

27_06cSynapticCleft_U.jpg

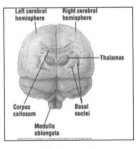

27_07SynapticTerminals_CL.jpg

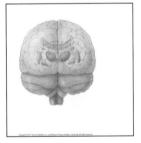

27_07SynapticTerminals_CNL.jpg

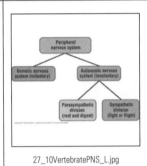

27_08VertNervousSyst_L.jpg

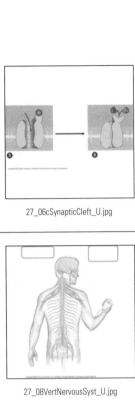

27_08VertNervousSyst_U.jpg

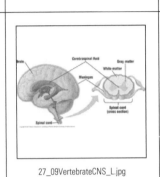

27_09VertebrateCNS_L.jpg

27_09VertebrateCNS_U.jpg

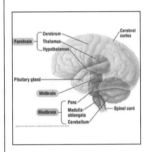

27_10VertebratePNS_L.jpg

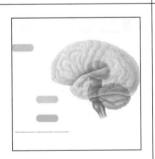

27_10VertebratePNS_U.jpg

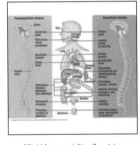

27_11AutonomicNervSys_L.jpg

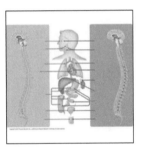

27_11AutonomicNervSys_U.jpg

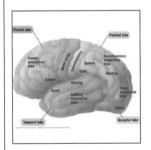

27_12HumanBrainStruct_L.jpg

27_12HumanBrainStruct_U.jpg

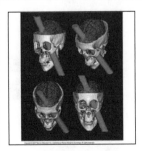

27_13BrainRear_L.jpg

27_13BrainRear_U.jpg

27_14LeftHemisphere_L.jpg

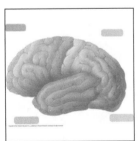

27_14LeftHemisphere_U.jpg

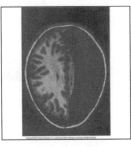

27_15Hemispherectomy_UP.jpg

27_16PhineasGage_UP.jpg

27_17TasteBud1_L.jpg

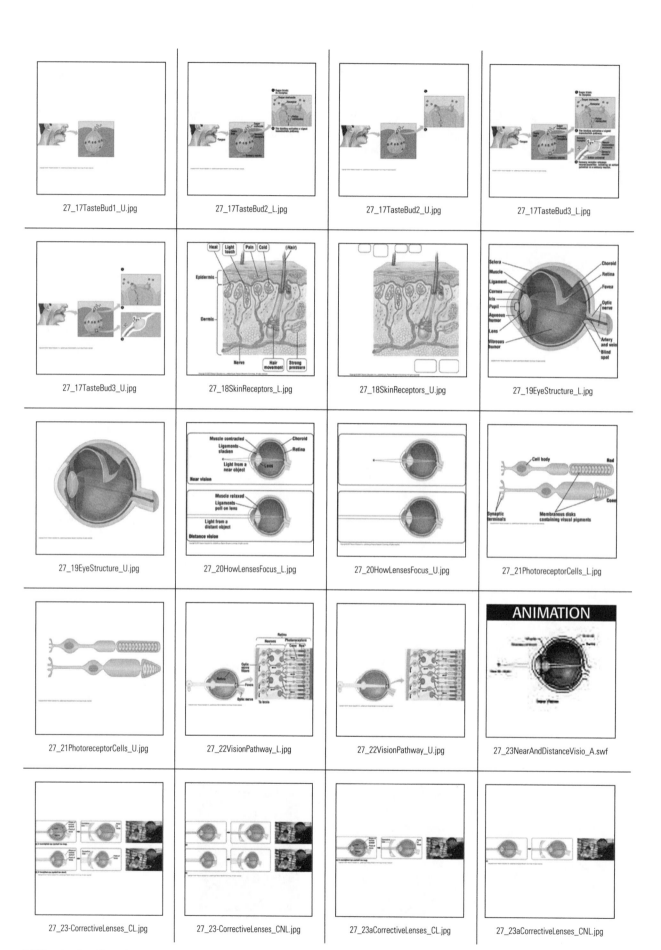

27_17TasteBud1_U.jpg

27_17TasteBud2_L.jpg

27_17TasteBud2_U.jpg

27_17TasteBud3_L.jpg

27_17TasteBud3_U.jpg

27_18SkinReceptors_L.jpg

27_18SkinReceptors_U.jpg

27_19EyeStructure_L.jpg

27_19EyeStructure_U.jpg

27_20HowLensesFocus_L.jpg

27_20HowLensesFocus_U.jpg

27_21PhotoreceptorCells_L.jpg

27_21PhotoreceptorCells_U.jpg

27_22VisionPathway_L.jpg

27_22VisionPathway_U.jpg

27_23NearAndDistanceVisio_A.swf

27_23-CorrectiveLenses_CL.jpg

27_23-CorrectiveLenses_CNL.jpg

27_23aCorrectiveLenses_CL.jpg

27_23aCorrectiveLenses_CNL.jpg

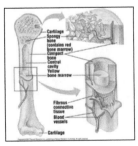

27_23bCorrectiveLenses_CL.jpg

27_23bCorrectiveLenses_CNL.jpg

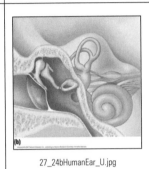

27_24-HumanEar_L.jpg

27_24-HumanEar_U.jpg

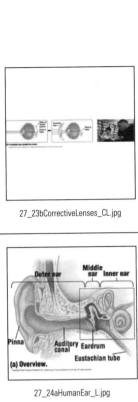

27_24aHumanEar_L.jpg

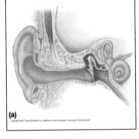

27_24aHumanEar_U.jpg

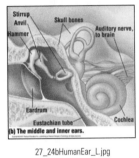

27_24bHumanEar_L.jpg

27_24bHumanEar_U.jpg

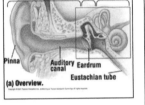

27_25OrganOfCorti_L.jpg

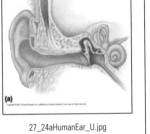

27_25OrganOfCorti_U.jpg

27_26SoundThroughEar_L.jpg

27_26SoundThroughEar_U.jpg

27_27HumanEndoskeleton_L.jpg

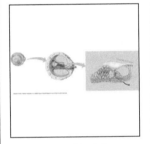

27_27HumanEndoskeleton_U.jpg

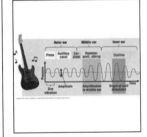

27_28Joints_L.jpg

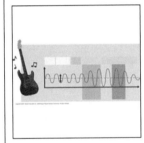

27_28Joints_U.jpg

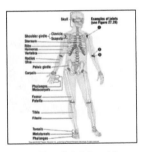

27_29ArmBone_L.jpg

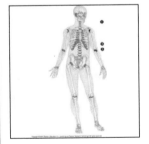

27_29ArmBone_U.jpg

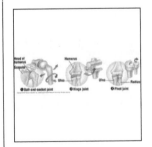

27_30BrokenBone_UP.jpg

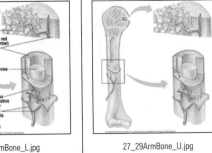

27_31AntagonisticAction_L.jpg

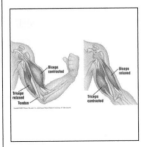
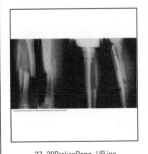

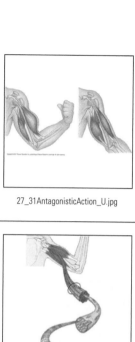

27_31AntagonisticAction_U.jpg

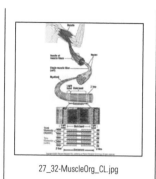

27_32-MuscleOrg_CL.jpg

27_32-MuscleOrg_CNL.jpg

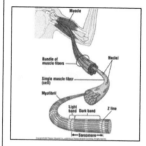

27_32aMuscleOrg_L.jpg

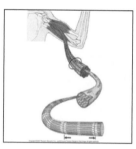

27_32aMuscleOrg_U.jpg

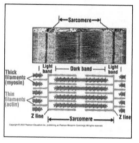

27_32bMuscleOrg_CL.jpg

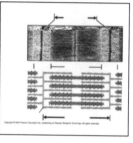

27_32bMuscleOrg_CNL.jpg

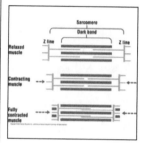

27_33SlidingFilModel_L.jpg

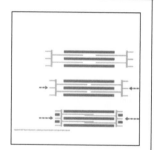

27_33SlidingFilModel_U.jpg

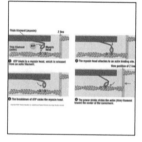

27_34SlidingFilMechs_L.jpg

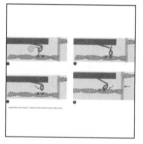

27_34SlidingFilMechs_U.jpg

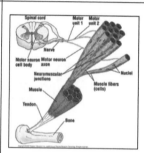

27_35MotorUnit_L.jpg

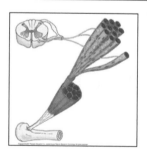

27_35MotorUnit_U.jpg

27_36Athlete_UP.jpg

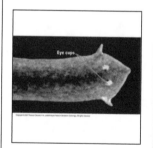

27_37Planarian_LP.jpg

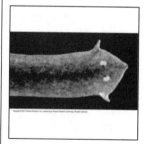

27_37Planarian_UP.jpg

27_T01BrainStructure_T.jpg

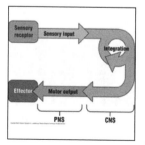

27_UN614aNevSysOrg_L.jpg

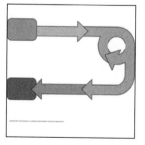

27_UN614aNevSysOrg_U.jpg

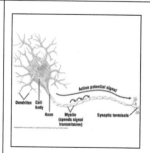

27_UN614bNeurons_L.jpg

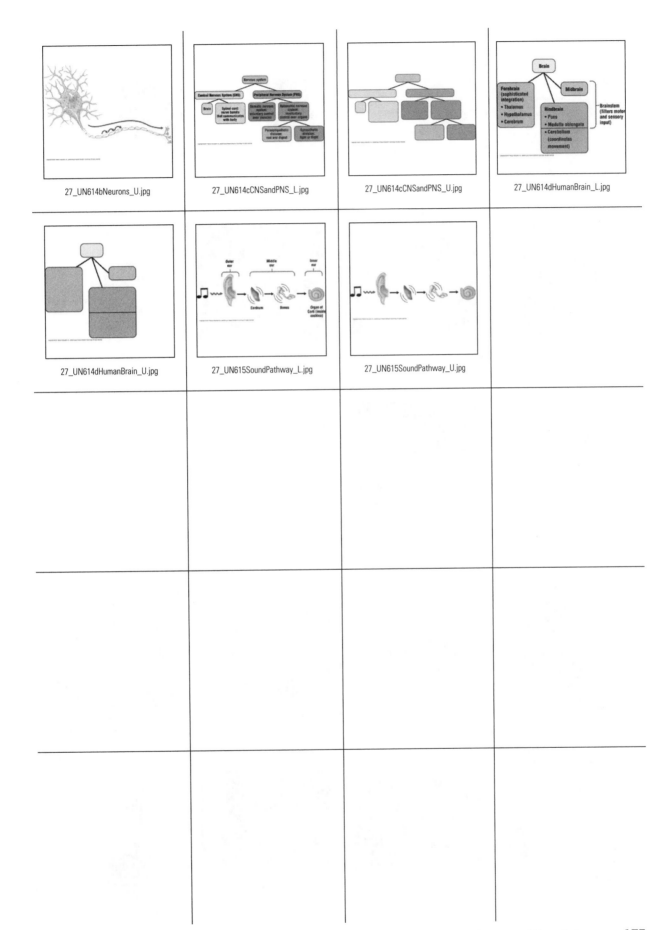

27_UN614bNeurons_U.jpg

27_UN614cCNSandPNS_L.jpg

27_UN614cCNSandPNS_U.jpg

27_UN614dHumanBrain_L.jpg

27_UN614dHumanBrain_U.jpg

27_UN615SoundPathway_L.jpg

27_UN615SoundPathway_U.jpg

28_00aHummingbird_LP.jpg

28_00bClonedPlant_LP.jpg

28_00cFlower_LP.jpg

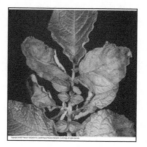

28_00dPollen_LP.jpg

28_01-PotatoRot_UP.jpg

28_01aPotatoRot_UP.jpg

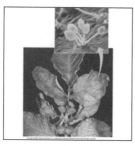

28_01bPotatoRot_UP.jpg

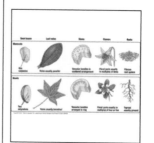

28_02MonocotDicot_L.jpg

28_02MonocotDicot_U.jpg

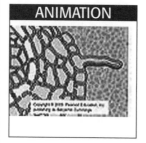

28_03MineralsFromSoil_A.swf

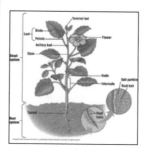

28_03PlantBody_L.jpg

28_03PlantBody_U.jpg

28_04SugarBeet_UP.jpg

28_05PruningEffects_LP.jpg

28_05PruningEffects_UP.jpg

28_06-ModifiedStems_LP.jpg

28_06-ModifiedStems_UP.jpg

28_06aModifiedStems_LP.jpg

28_06aModifiedStems_UP.jpg

28_06bModifiedStems_LP.jpg

28_06bModifiedStems_UP.jpg

28_06cModifiedStems_LP.jpg

28_06cModifiedStems_UP.jpg

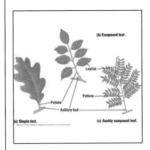

28_07SimpleVsCompound_L.jpg

28_07SimpleVsCompound_U.jpg

28_08-ModifiedLeaves_LP.jpg

28_08-ModifiedLeaves_UP.jpg

28_08aModifiedLeaves_LP.jpg

28_08aModifiedLeaves_UP.jpg

28_08bModifiedLeaves_LP.jpg

28_08bModifiedLeaves_UP.jpg

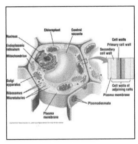

28_09PlantCellStructure_L.jpg

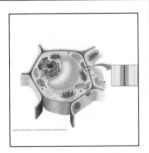

28_09PlantCellStructure_U.jpg

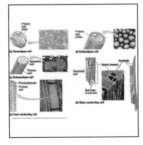

28_10-PlantCellTypes_CL.jpg

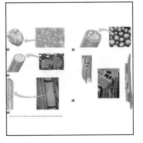

28_10-PlantCellTypes_CNL.jpg

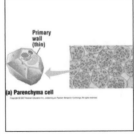

28_10aPlantCellTypes_CL.jpg

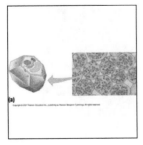

28_10aPlantCellTypes_CNL.jpg

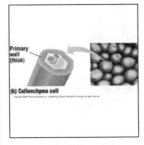

28_10bPlantCellTypes_CL.jpg

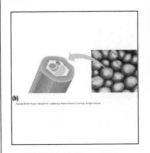

28_10bPlantCellTypes_CNL.jpg

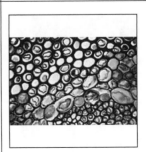

28_10bxCollenchymaCell_XUP.jpg

28_10cPlantCellTypes_L.jpg

28_10cPlantCellTypes_U.jpg

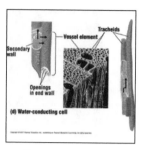

28_10dPlantCellTypes_CL.jpg

28_10dPlantCellTypes_CNL.jpg

28_10dxVesselElements_XUP.jpg

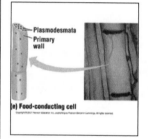

28_10ePlantCellTypes_CL.jpg

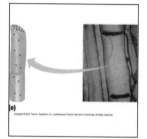

28_10ePlantCellTypes_CNL.jpg

28_11TissueSystems_L.jpg

28_11TissueSystems_U.jpg

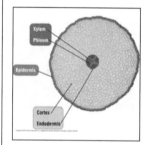

28_12DicotRootTissue_L.jpg

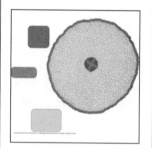

28_12DicotRootTissue_U.jpg

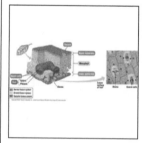

28_13-LeafTissue_CL.jpg

28_13-LeafTissue_CNL.jpg

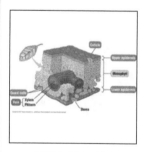

28_13aLeafTissue_L.jpg

28_13aLeafTissue_U.jpg

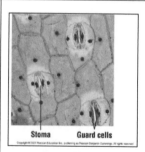

28_13bLeafTissue_LP.jpg

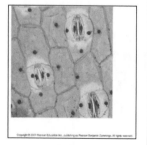

28_13bLeafTissue_UP.jpg

28_14-PlantLifeSpans_LP.jpg

28_14-PlantLifeSpans_UP.jpg

28_14aPlantLifeSpans_LP.jpg

28_14aPlantLifeSpans_UP.jpg

28_14bPlantLifeSpans_LP.jpg

28_14bPlantLifeSpans_UP.jpg

28_14cPlantLifeSpans_LP.jpg

28_14cPlantLifeSpans_UP.jpg

28_15MeristemGrowth_L.jpg

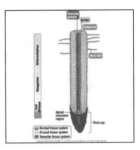

28_15MeristemGrowth_U.jpg

28_16RootGrowth_L.jpg

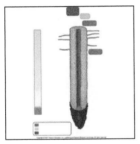

28_16RootGrowth_U.jpg

28_16TimeLapseRoot_SV.mpg

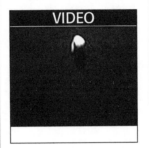

28_16TimeLapseRoot_VT.swf

28_16xRootTip_XUP.jpg

28_17StemGrowth1_L.jpg

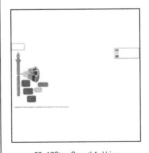

28_17StemGrowth1_U.jpg

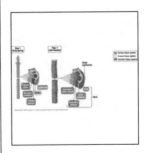

28_17StemGrowth2_L.jpg

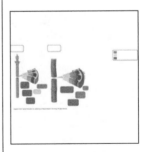

28_17StemGrowth2_U.jpg

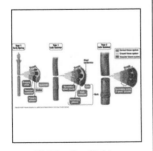

28_17StemGrowth3_L.jpg

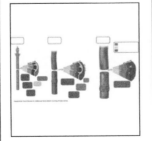

28_17StemGrowth3_U.jpg

28_17x1SecondXylmPhloem_XUP.jpg

28_17x2StemAnatomy_XUP.jpg

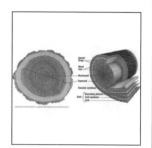

28_18LogAnatomy_CL.jpg

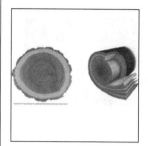

28_18LogAnatomy_CNL.jpg

28_19-AsexualPlantRepro_LP.jpg

28_19-AsexualPlantRepro_UP.jpg

28_19aAsexualPlantRepro_LP.jpg

28_19aAsexualPlantRepro_UP.jpg

28_19bAsexualPlantRepro_LP.jpg

28_19bAsexualPlantRepro_UP.jpg

28_19cAsexualPlantRepro_LP.jpg

28_19cAsexualPlantRepro_UP.jpg

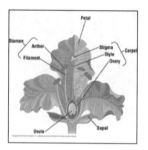

28_20FlowerStructure_L.jpg

28_20FlowerStructure_U.jpg

28_20FlowerTimeLapse_SV.mpg

28_20FlowerTimeLapse_VT.swf

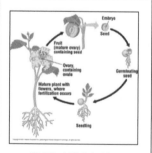

28_21AngioLifeCycle_L.jpg

28_21AngioLifeCycle_U.jpg

28_21PlantTimeLapse_SV.mpg

28_21PlantTimeLapse_VT.swf

28_22Gametophytes1_L.jpg

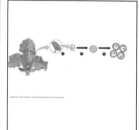

28_22Gametophytes1_U.jpg

28_22Gametophytes2_L.jpg

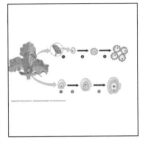

28_22Gametophytes2_U.jpg

28_23PlantFertilization_A.swf

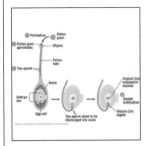

28_23DoubleFertilization_L.jpg

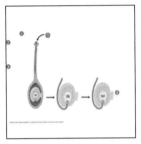

28_23DoubleFertilization_U.jpg

28_24aFruitDevelopment_A.swf

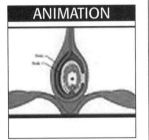

28_24aSeedDevelopment_A.swf

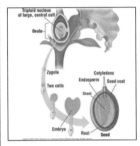

28_24SeedDevelopment_L.jpg

28_24SeedDevelopment_U.jpg

28_25PeaPodDevt_UP.jpg

28_26Fruit_UP.jpg

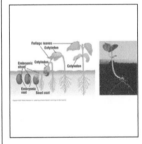

28_27BeanGermination_CL.jpg

28_27BeanGermination_CNL.jpg

28_28BeePollination_UP.jpg

28_28BatPollinating_SV.mpg

28_28BatPollinating_VT.swf

28_28BeePollinating_SV.mpg

28_28BeePollinating_VT.swf

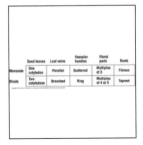

28_UN637aMonocotDicot_L.jpg

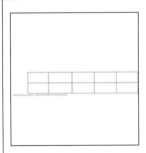

28_UN637aMonocotDicot_U.jpg

CHAPTER 28   The Life of a Flowering Plant   **179**

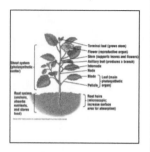

28_UN637bPlantOrgans_L.jpg

28_UN637bPlantOrgans_U.jpg

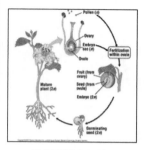

28_UN638lifeCycle_L.jpg

28_UN638LifeCycle_U.jpg

29_00aOrganicFarm_LP.jpg

29_00bSunflower_LP.jpg

29_00cMapleTree_LP.jpg

29_00dMapleSyrup_LP.jpg

29_01OrganicFarm_UP.jpg

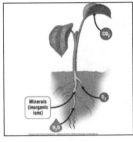

29_02NutrUptake_L.jpg

29_02NutrUptake_U.jpg

29_02SunDewTrapPrey_SV.mpg

29_02SunDewTrapPrey_VT.swf

29_03BeechTree_UP.jpg

29_04NitroRichSoil_UP.jpg

29_05-NutrientDeficiencs_LP.jpg

29_05-NutrientDeficiencs_UP.jpg

29_05aNutrientDeficiency_LP.jpg

29_05aNutrientDeficiency_UP.jpg

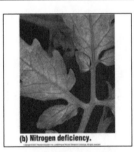

29_05bNutrientDeficiency_LP.jpg

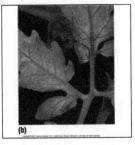

29_05bNutrientDeficiency_UP.jpg

29_05cNutrientDeficiencs_LP.jpg

29_05cNutrientDeficiency_UP.jpg

29_05dNutrientDeficiency_LP.jpg

29_05dNutrientDeficiency_UP.jpg

29_06RootHairs_UP.jpg

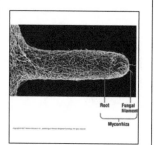

29_07Mycorrhiza_LP.jpg

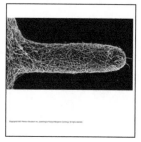

29_07Mycorrhiza_UP.jpg

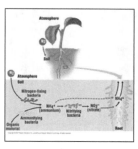

29_08NitroBacteria_L.jpg

29_08NitroBacteria_U.jpg

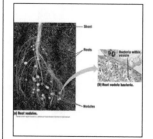

29_09-RootNodules_LP.jpg

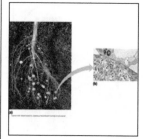

29_09-RootNodules_UP.jpg

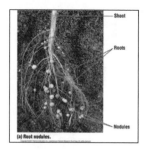

29_09aRootNodules_LP.jpg

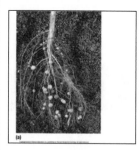

29_09aRootNodules_UP.jpg

29_09axRootNodulesMacro_XUP.jpg

29_09bRootNodules_LP.jpg

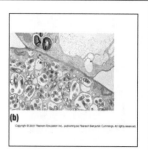

29_09bRootNodules_UP.jpg

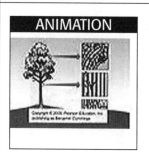

29_10Transpiration_A.swf

29_10TransportInRoots_A.swf

29_10WaterUptake1_L.jpg

29_10WaterUptake1_U.jpg

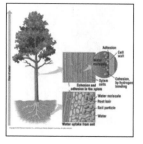

29_10WaterUptake2_L.jpg

29_10WaterUptake2_U.jpg

29_10WaterUptake3_L.jpg

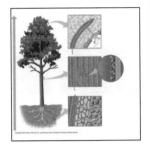

29_10WaterUptake3_U.jpg

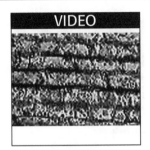

29_11GuardCells_L.jpg

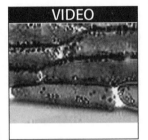

29_11GuardCells_U.jpg

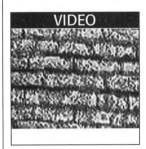

29_11Plasmolysis_SV.mpg

29_11Plasmolysis_VT.swf

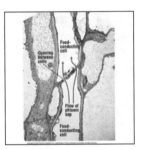

29_11TurgidElodea_SV.mpg

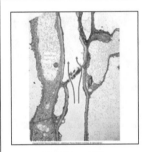

29_11TurgidElodea_VT.swf

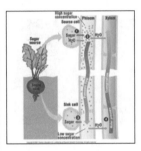

29_12PhloemTranslocSpr_A.swf

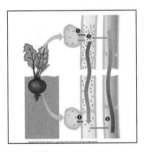

29_12PhloemTranslocSum_A.swf

29_12Phloem_LP.jpg

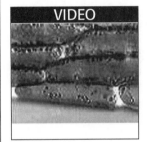

29_12Phloem_UP.jpg

29_13PressureFlow_L.jpg

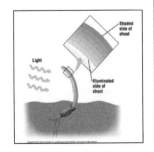

29_13PressureFlow_U.jpg

29_14Phototropism_UP.jpg

29_14Phototropism_SV.mpg

29_14Phototropism_VT.swf

29_15PhototropGrass_L.jpg

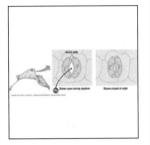

29_15PhototropGrass_U.jpg

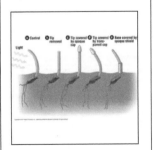

29_16PhototropExper_L.jpg

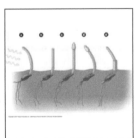

29_16PhototropExper_U.jpg

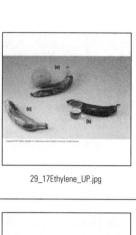

29_17Ethylene_UP.jpg

29_18Gibberellin_UP.jpg

29_19ABAremoval_UP.jpg

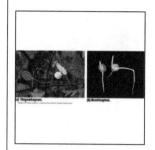

29_20-Tropisms_LP.jpg

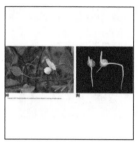

29_20-Tropisms_UP.jpg

29_20aTropisms_LP.jpg

29_20aTropisms_UP.jpg

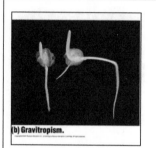

29_20bTropisms_LP.jpg

29_20bTropisms_UP.jpg

29_20aGravitropism_SV.mpg

29_20aGravitropism_VT.swf

29_20bMimosaLeaf_SV.mpg

29_20bMimosaLeaf_VT.swf

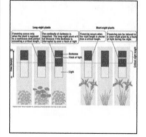

29_21Photoperiod_L.jpg

29_21Photoperiod_U.jpg

29_22DevilFlowerMantis_UP.jpg

29_T01PlantHormones_T.jpg

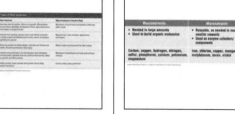

29_UN656aPlantNutrition_L.jpg

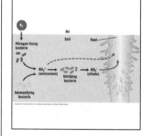

29_UN656bNitroNutrition_L.jpg

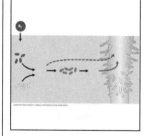

29_UN656bNitroNutrition_U.jpg

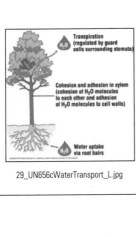

29_UN656cWaterTransport_L.jpg

29_UN656cWaterTransport_U.jpg

29xSundewPlant_XUP.jpg